BAWDY BALLADS & DIRTY DITTIES
OF THE WARTIME RAF

First edition
Published in 2000 by
WOODFIELD PUBLISHING
Bognor Regis, West Sussex PO21 5EL UK

© The Contributors, 2000

ISBN 0 873203 69 1

Bawdy Ballads & Dirty Ditties

of the Wartime RAF

Compiled by

HAROLD BENNETT

Woodfield *Publishing*

BOGNOR REGIS · WEST SUSSEX · ENGLAND

Preface

This is the first edition of *Bawdy Ballads & Dirty Ditties*, and although a great deal of time and trouble has gone into its creation, there may be errors or omissions in some of the lyrics as printed here.

If you can suggest any corrections/alterations/additions to the material contained herein, or know of any other ditties or ballads that should have been included, please let us know.

Write to: Editorial Dept
Woodfield Publishing
Bognor Regis
PO21 5EL
United Kingdom

email to: submissions@woodfieldpublishing.com

Introduction

It is odd that two of us, Ted Bowles and I, wrote to the Editor of *Intercom* at exactly the same time on the same subject: the 'dirty ditties' and 'bawdy ballads' that were sung in Aircrew Messes during World War 2. It had not occurred to me that I might land the job of collecting the whole lot!

People have been most helpful in submitting a large amount of such stuff. Many thanks to all, worldwide. Thanks in particular to Gordon Collett who sent his hand-written "Wop/AG's Bible" of eighty or so rude songs and to Gerhard Heilig of Vienna (who <u>was</u> in the RAF!) who sent me another fortyish. I say "another" with some abandon, because some songs exist in such a wide variety of versions that they are virtually completely different from each other. Several appear in this book in their various forms. Other semi-duplicates I have merged, showing the variations in brackets.

At times it has been hard work typing them in. It's difficult to roll around on the floor laughing and keep typing!

To save space, I have kept the presentation as simple as possible. For example choruses (sung between verses) are simply labelled CHORUS – with the words of the chorus in italics – easy!

It is strange that the biggest response related to a poem that is probably not of RAF origin at all: 'Boidies' (*see page 25*). Nobody seems to know where this rhyme originated, but hopefully the version included here is now complete.

Thank you everybody who contributed!

Harold Bennett, November 2000

Alphabetical Index

504 Auxiliary Squadron 30
A Little Bit 57
A Shilling a Go 112
Abdul Abulbul Emir 241
Advice 161
Aircrew Cadets' Lament, An 144
Aircrew Chum 19
Airman's Prayer, The 233
Albert 134
Alderman's Daughters, The 302
Alice Tucker 180
All The Nice Girls Love a Candle 205
Alouette 208
Analysis of a Man 127
Anthony Roley or ABC 256
Anti-War Panacea 44
Archibald Clare or the Jugulaire 60
Arse-End Charlie 33
Arsehole, Charcoal 300
Arseholes Are Cheap Today 197
As one goes by 22
Aubade For The Shithouse 255
B Flight 218
Babe That I Carry, The 313
Baby Carriage 58
Ball of Kirriemuir, The # 1 166
Ball Of Kirriemuir, The #2 168
Ballad Of Eskimo Nell, The 117
Balls of O'Leary, The 146
Barracuda II 23
Bastard King of England, The 65
Behind Those Swinging Doors 283
Belting Down the Runway 53
Bengal Blues 272
Benghazi Mail Run, The 186
Bless 'em All 29
Blinded by Shit 69
Bloody Great Wheel, The 40
Bloody Hell 70
Boat Ballad 260

Boidies 25
Bold Aviator, The 18
Bollocks! 128
Bollocky Bill the Sailor 68
Boy Meets Girl 73
Brian Boru 71
Bricklayers' Union, The 289
Briefing, The 27
Brown Eyes 88
Butchers 79
Call up Blues 16
Chandler's Shop, The 87
Chastity Belt, The 181
Chicago 89
Chin Chin Chinaman 97
Choric Song of the Masturbators, The 237
Cocaine Bill 92
Cold 194
Come on and Join 21
Come on Boys 72
Cowboy's Whore, The 304
Craven A 94
Crayfish, The 95
Cuando Caliente El Sol 153
Daily Prayer 136
Daniel and the King 199
Darkie Sunday School 96
D-Day Dodgers 31
Deadeye Dick (Again) 107
Definitions 99
Diamond Lily 189
Did You Ever See? 289
Dinah, Dinah, Show Us Your Leg 101
Dirge of 849, The 102
Dirty Gertie 187
Do Your Balls Hang Low? 304
Doggies' Meeting, The 107
Don't Say No 268
Down by the Barrack Gate 142
Dual Control 146
Duchess of Lee, The 238
Durex Is A Girl's Best Friend 126
Fairey! Fairey! 23
Family Called Stein, A 148
Fanny Bay 113

Bawdy Ballads

Farmer's Dog, The 105
Farting Competition, The 129
Father's Grave 145
Fifty-One Squadron 45
Foggy Foggy Dew, The 136
For Johnny (1942) 16
Forty thousand Fortresses 26
Frankie and Johnnie 138
Gay Caballero, The 74
Gay Caballeroo #2 75
Gentlemen Should Please Refrain 279
Get Hold of This 116
Good Old Beer 274
Good Ship Venus, The 295
Grace 143
Grace #2 143
Grandad's Grave 144
Great Plenipotentiary, The 224
Group HQ 37
Gungda Din 293
Hard Cider 53
Harlot of Jerusalem, The 154
He Tried Me on the Sofa 221
Hedgehog, The 148
Hedgehog, The (Again!) 149
Here's to the breezes 234
Hole in the Elephant's Bottom, The 115
Honolulu Penny 183
How Ashamed I Was 50
How Much to Oldham? 218
How the Money Rolls In 200
I Don't Want to Join the Air Force 17
I Don't Want to Join the Army 17
I Dreamed My Love 111
I Haven't Seen Old Hitler 45
I Owe me Darlin' 91
I Took My Wife For A Scramble 268
I've Got Sixpence 273
If 151
If I Were The Marrying Kind 190
In Matruh 197
In Mobile 195
In the Violet Time 232
It's foolish but it's fun 35

Ivan Skavinsky Skavar 239
John Thomas 284
Joys of Copulation, The 80
Katukarunda 61
Keyhole in the Door 162
Keyhole in the Door #2 163
Kidney Wiper, The 164
Kiss Me Goodnight Sergeant Major 270
Lady Astor's Speech 219
Lady Jane 175
Large Balls 56
Last Class 264
Last Saturday Night 266
Letitia has a Large One 178
Life Presents a Dismal Picture 104
Lilian Barker 179
Little Angeline 62
Little Jim 160
Little Mildred 125
Little Sally 125
Long Strong Black Pudding 282
Lord St Clancy 259
Love One 251
Lulu 182
Lydia Pink 184
Mad Carew 78
Malaya 188
Mary Box 247
Mary had a Little Lamb 161
Mary Was A Good Girl 192
Mayor of Bayswater's Daughter, The 67
Me No Likee Blitish Sairor 270
Modern Meteorologist, The 32
Mole Catcher, The 198
Monk of Great Renown, The 204
Monte Carlo 205
Mr Codfish And Mr Sole 66
Mr Pupil and Mr Instructor 42
My Darling Clementine 90
My Grandfather's Cock 93
My Husband 150
My Jenny Wren Wedding 152
My Little Pink Panties 221
My Love Is For A Bold Marine 189

● ●

Bawdy Ballads

My Old Flo 275
My Ring A-Rang A-Roo 250
Nellie 'Awkins 59
Nelson and Hood 208
Nemesis 76
Nightwatchman 114
No Balls At All 211
No Balls At All #2 212
North Atlantic Squadron 54
O'Reilly's Daughter 248
Ode to the Four Letter Word 213
Ode to the Four Letter Word #2 215
Old Apple Tree, The 131
Old Boy 206
Old Farmer, The 98
Old-Fashioned Hali, An 38
Old-Fashioned Wimpey, An 38
Old King Cole 46
Old King Cole #2 48
Old King Cole #3 49
Old Monk, The 203
Old Red Flannel Drawers that Maggie Wore, The 108
Old Woman Of Dublin, The 113
Ollie, Ollie, Ollie 214
On Ilkley Moor Bar t'at 159
On Monday I touched her on the ankle 59
Once There Was a Servant Girl 275
One Fish Ball 133
One of the Few 132
Ops In A Whitley 33
Ops In A Wimpey 33
Our Flight Sergeant 39
Pacific Lament 216
Passengers will please refrain #1 278
Passengers will please refrain #2 278
Penguin 220
Pickeldy Pickeldy Pox 222
Pig Song, The 223
Please Don't Burn Our Shithouse Down 272
Poor Blind Nell 64
Portions of a Woman, The 310
Pump Away 176
Puritan Mathyas, The 242
Quartermaster's Stores, The 14

Queen of all the Fairies 290
Questions & Answers 243
Rajah-Sahib of Astrakhan, The 280
Ram of Derbyshire, The 245
Rape 246
Red Riding Hood 247
Ring The Bell, Verger 228
Ring-A-Dang-Do 252
Rip My Knickers Away 253
Roedean School.. 254
Roll Me Over 257
Roll Me Over In The Clover #2 259
Roll Your Leg Over 262
Salome 261
Salome #2 263
Salvation Army 264
Sammy Hall 265
Scapa Flow... 41
Second Oldest Profession, The 126
Seven Whores Of Pompey 305
Shaibah Blues 41
She had to go and Lose it at the Astor 51
She Was Poor But She Was Honest.. 229
She Went for a Ride in a Morgan 206
She'll be Coming Round the Mountain 207
Single-Engined Basket 15
Sister Lily 110
Some Die Of Drinking Water 103
Song Of The Gremlins 24
Sonia Snell 276
Sour grapes?.. 162
Souse Family, The 244
Sparrer, The 274
Spitfire Story, A 36
Story of P/O Prune, The 235
Street in Cairo, A 77
Street of a Thousand Arseholes 285
Street of a Thousand Arseholes #2 286
Sunday, Monday Or Always 267
Sweet Violets 271
Thanks for the Memory 30
That Lovely Weekend 303
The 'ole in the Ark 209
The Boy Stood on the Burning Deck 97
The Fucking Thing Was Ours!... 314

The Girls I like 103
The Walrus and the Carpenter 135
There Was A Priest 234
There's A Home For Batchy Airmen 34
There's no AMO about Love 20
They Called the Bastard Stephen 309
They Say There's A ... Just Leaving 177
They're Pulling The Old Pub Down 236
This Old Coat of Mine 217
Those Foolish Things 137
Three German Officers Crossed the Rhine 140
Three Harlots of Baghdad 269
Three Old Ladies 287
Three Old Whores from Winnipeg 308
Tiger Lil 188
Tree of Life, The 291
True Love 292
Twenty Toes 133
Uncle Dick and Auntie Mabel 185
Valley of the Ruhr, The 15
Valleys of Assam, The 147
Venal Vera 294
Virgin Sturgeon 85
WAAF's Lament, A 233
Walking in a Meadow Green 193
We are the Air Sea Rescue 28
We are the Heavy Bombers 52
We are the Royal Air Force 28
We're a shower of bastards 234
West Virginian Hills 312
When She Was Only Seventeen 308
When this Bloody War is Over 151
Whiffenpoof Song, The 301
Whore from Baroda, A 97
Why? 183
Will You Marry Me? 307
Winter Nights 277
With It In 222
Woodpecker Song, The 311
Yorkshire Airfield, A 202
You go to Hamburg and I'll go to Essen 28
Young Lady from Nantes, A 128
Young Man of Zerubbubell, A 281
Youngest Child, The 57
Your Baby has Gone Dahn the Plug'ole 227

The Quartermaster's Stores

This must be the most popular of all the wartime sing-along songs although it has nothing to do with the RAF. It comes from the trenches in World War One. I don't suppose that there is anybody in the world who hasn't heard it before! Here is a brief reminder of the verses for old time's sake.

There are rats, rats, rats as big as alley cats,
In the store, in the store,
There are rats, rats, rats as big as alley cats,
In the quartermaster's store.

Chorus   *My eyes are dim I cannot see,*
                    I have not brought my specs with me,
                    I have not brought my specs with me.

There is ham, ham mixed up with jam, *in the store etc*

There is beer, beer, lots of blooming beer... *etc*

There is cheese, cheese, wafting in the breeze... *etc*

There is bread, bread, heavy as lumps of lead... *etc*

There is whisky, whiskey, the stuff that makes you frisky... *etc*

There are socks, socks, filthy smelly socks... *etc*

There are tents, tents, full of holes and rents... *etc*

There is rice, rice, full of bugs and lice... *etc*

There are flies, flies, eating all the pies... *etc*

The Valley of the Ruhr

The World War II, RAF Bomber Command Aircrew version,
sung to the tune of 'The Quartermaster's Stores'

There was flak, flak, bags of bloody flak
In the Ruhr, in the Ruhr,
There was flak, flak, bags of bloody flak
In the Valley of the Ruhr.

Chorus *My eyes are dim I cannot see,*
     The searchlights they have blinded me,
     The searchlights they have blinded me.

There were fighters, fighters, bags of bloody fighters,
In the Ruhr, in the Ruhr,
There were fighters, fighters, bags of bloody fighters,
In the Valley of the Ruhr.

There was twitch, twitch, bags of bloody twitch,
In the Ruhr *etc etc*

There was panic, panic, bags of bloody panic,
In the Ruhr *etc etc*

A Single-Engined Basket

A tisket, a tasket, a single-engined basket.
They wrote a letter to my Mum
And told her I had crashed it.
I crashed it, I crashed it,
That single-engined basket.
I turned on finals, yanked the stick,
Son of a bitch, I snapped it,
I snapped it, I snapped it,
That single-engined basket.
A two-turn spin, I torque-stalled in.
Oh, Jesus! How I smashed it!

For Johnny (1942)

Do not despair
For Johnny head in air
He sleeps as sound
As Johnny underground.

Fetch out no shroud
For Johnny in the cloud
And keep your tears
For him in after years.

Better by far
For Johnny the bright star
To keep your head
And see his children fed.

John Pudney

Call up Blues

Call up the Army and the Navy,
Call up the rank and file.
Call up the Gallant Territorials.
They'll face danger with a smile.

Call up the Boys of the Old Brigade
To keep Olde England free.
You can call up my Mother,
My Sister or my Brother,
But for Christ's Sake don't call me!

I Don't Want to Join the Air Force

I don't want to join the Air Force,
I don't want to go to war,
I'd rather hang around Piccadilly Underground,
Living off the earnings of a high born lady.

I don't need no Froggy women,
London's full of girls I never 'ad,
I want to stay in Blighty,
Lord Gawd Almighty
Following in the footsteps of me Dad.

I don't want a bullet up my arsehole,
I don't want my bollocks shot away,
I'd rather live in England,
Merry, merry England,
And fornicate my bleeding life away.

I Don't Want to Join the Army

I don't want to join the Army,
I don't want to go to war.
I just want to hang around
Piccadilly Underground,
Livin' off the life of a high priced lady!

I don't want a bayonet up my arsehole,
I don't want my bollocks shot away.
I'd sooner live in England,
Not-so-merry England,
And fritter all my fucking life away.

The Bold Aviator

(Tune – The Tarpaulin Jacket)

This has the strongest claim to be the oldest flying song of all, irrespective of Service. There were many versions and variants throughout the 1914-1918 war and even in the 1939-1945 period there was an up-dated form with mention of the 20mm cannon shell and radial engine. But the song was apparently extant as long ago as 1912 when the legendary Commander Samson became the first RN Aviator to fly off a ship. This is but one version.

Oh, the bold aviator was dying,
And as 'neath the wreckage he lay, he lay,
To the sobbing me-chanics about him,
These last parting words he did say...

CHORUS *Two valve springs you'll find in my stomach,*
Three spark plugs are safe in my lung, my lung,
The prop is in splinters inside me,
To my fingers the joy-stick has clung.

Oh, had I the wings of a little dove,
Far a-way, far a-way would I fly, I fly,
Straight to the arms of my true-love,
And there would I lay me and die.

Take the propeller boss out of my liver,
Take the aileron out of my thigh, my thigh,
From the seat of my pants take the piston,
Then see if the old crate will fly.

Then get you two little white tombstones,
Put them one at my head and my toe, my toe,
And get you a penknife and scratch there,
"Here lies a poor pilot below."

Take the cylinders out of my kidneys,
The connecting-rod out of my brain, my brain,
From the small of my back get the crankshaft,
And assemble the engine again.

Bawdy Ballads

And when at the Court of Enquiry
They ask for the reason I died, I died,
Please say I forgot twice iota
Was the minimum angle of glide.

Take the cylinders out of my kidneys,
The connecting-rod out of my brain, my brain,
From the small of my back get the crankshaft,
And assemble the engine again.

Aircrew Chum

A poor Wop/AG lay a dying
At the end of a bright Summer's day,
His comrades were gathered around him,
To wash all the bloodstains away.

Take the bullet from out of my shoulder,
Take the shrapnel out of my brain,
And the pom-pom from out of my liver,
And patch up the turret again.

I'll be riding a cloud in the morning,
No more this gun turret to cuss,
So please patch me up in my shroud,
For I'll not be needing this bus.

So hold all your glasses steady,
And let's drink a toast to the sky,
For here's to the dead already,
And here's to the next man to die.

There's no AMO about Love

(AMO = Air Ministry Order)

Sir Archibald, I really am in quite a shocking flap,
So will you, just for my sake, be an awfully decent chap?
You see, Sir A, the trouble's really this, I have a girl,
And what with this and that she's got me in quite a whirl.
Now you, and several other blokes, as everybody knows,
Think up those helpful little pamphlets known as AMOs,
But honestly, Sir Archibald, there's something gravely lacking,
So will you call a conference and get your chappies cracking?

CHORUS
There's no AMO about love.
You've missed out nothing else from rats to rations:
But I've searched for days and days
Through the "N"s and through the "A"s
And I can't find any ruling on the tender passions.
There's advice on bites of tse-tse flies in most peculiar places,
What not to say if AOCs produce more than four aces,
And there's how to serve spaghetti to a sheik in an oasis,
But there's no AMO about love.

I'm sure you'll see the danger, Sir, we all go off on leave,
So many of us, young, untried, unsullied and naive.
We're lured by siren voices and we finish up as wrecks,
At the mercy of what laughingly is called the weaker sex.
So I suggest an AMO, and please don't think it cheek,
On "Love and All About It" – with Appendix on Technique,
Or p'raps you could amend KRs, they need a bit of checking,
Insert a Para somewhere on the gentle art of necking.

CHORUS
There's no AMO about love.
You really must admit it's rather stupid.
There are several slightly odd
Little hints on salted cod,
There are lots and lots on swill, but not a thing on Cupid.

There's one on station libraries, and two on station cats,
A slightly nauseating one on un-cooked mutton fats,
There's what to do with gas-capes, and what not to do with ATS,
But there's no AMO about love...

There's no AMO about love.
There's gardening and garbage pails and ENSA,
But if someone waves a wand and you meet a lovely blonde,
Oh what to do and when and where, there's not a scrap of gen, Sir.
You burst into her boudoir and she's looking simply great,
You say "My darling love..." and see the other chap too late,
And she says, "My husband's home on unexpected forty-eight!"
There's no AMO about love...

There's one on boots knee rubber and there's one on ale and stout,
Some splendid sanitation hints on types inside and out
And there's how to bed a mule down in the Orkneys in a drought,
But there's no AMO about love...

Come on and Join

Come on and join, come on and join,
Come on and join the Royal Air Force.
Ten bob a week,
Nothing much to eat,
Great big boots and blisters on your feet.

Come on and join the Royal Air Force,
A' sitting on the grass,
A' polishing your brass,
Great big spiders crawling up your arse.
Come on and join the Royal Air Force!

As one goes by

(Tune – As Time Goes By)

It's called the Barracuda
And nothing could be cruder
Still flying in the sky.
You really can't believe it's true
As one goes by.

Observer and Air-Gunner
Weigh down this seven-tonner,
And they will tell you why
They're happy to be on the ground
As one goes by.

High-strutted tailplane
Very out of date,
Radar and wireless
Adding to the weight,
High wing and dive brakes
Such a fucking crate
Could never really fly.

That two ton pair of legs
Is just the bloody dregs,
That Fairey's can't deny.
The RAF just rub their eyes
As one goes by.

Fairey! Fairey!

(Tune – Daisy, Daisy)

Fairey! Fairey! Give me your answer do,
What is wrong with my Barracuda Two?
Dive-bombing has strained my structure,
I've got a stressed-skin rupture,
And rivets pop, along the top
And one of them might hit you.

Fairey! Fairey! What are we going to do?
Nine Wing's grounded, looks pretty bad for you.
When my Barra falls asunder
I'll be a wingless wonder.
I'll jump out quick, and bring my stick
And stuff it right up you!

Barracuda II

(Tune – Any Old Iron?)

Any old iron? Any old iron? Any, any, any old iron?
Talk about a treat
Torpedoing a fleet,
Any old cruiser or battleship you meet.
Weight six tons, no front guns,
Fuck-all to rely on.
You know what you can do
With your Barracuda Two
Old iron, old iron!

Any old iron? Any old iron? Any, any, any old iron?
The engine is a teased Rolls Royce,
A Merlin 32 and it ain't our choice
Open up the throttle
And the whole fucking lot'll
Wail like an air raid siren.
You know what you can do
With your Barracuda Two
Old iron, old iron!

Song Of The Gremlins

(Tune – Eton Boating Song)

This is the tale of the Gremlins
Told by the PRU
At Benson and Wick and St Eval
And believe me, you slobs, it is true.

When you're seven miles up in the Heavens
That's a hell of lonely spot
And it's fifty degrees below zero,
Which isn't exactly hot,

When you're frozen blue like your Spitfire,
And you're scared a Mosquito pink,
When you're thousands of miles from nowhere,
And there's nothing below but the drink.

It's then that you'll see the Gremlins,
Green and gamboge and gold,
Male and female and neuter,
Gremlins both young and old.

It's no good trying to dodge them,
The lessons you learned in the Link
Won't help you evade a Gremlin,
Though you boost and you dive and you jink.

White ones will wiggle your wing-tips,
Male ones will muddle your maps,
Green ones will guzzle your glycol,
Females will flutter your flaps,

Pink ones will perch on your Perspex
And dance pirouettes on your prop.
There's one spherical middle-aged Gremlin
Who spins on your stick like a top.

They'll freeze up your camera shutters,
They'll bite through your aileron wires,
They'll cause your whole tail to flutter,
(They'll bend and they'll break and they'll batter)
They'll insert toasting forks in your tyres.

This is the song of the Gremlins
As sung by the P.R.U.,
Pretty Ruddy Unlikely to many,
But fact, none the less, to the few.

Boidies

Thankyou EVERYONE who has helped with this intriguing rhyme

I first 'hoid' it in Canada, where I was trained on Harvards at No 2 SFTS RCAF Uplands Ottawa. Norman Lenton hoid it at No 7 ITW Newquay. It is strange that this rhyme has brought the biggest initial response although it was certainly not of RAF origin.

To be narrated in the broadest Bronx/Brooklyn accent:

De Spring iz sprung, de grass iz rizz,
Ah wonder where dem boidies iz.
Ma says dat in de Spring
De boids iz on de wing:
But dat's absoid,
Ah always hoid
De wings iz on de boid.

"Dat's not a boid ... it's a bird."
"Well, it choips like a boid."

Just WHO wrote this? Possibly no one knows.
Ah've trard hard enough over de yoirs to find out.
Just POSSIBLY the above is something like right?

Forty thousand Fortresses

(Tune: John Brown's Body)

Forty thousand Fortresses at forty thousand feet,
Forty thousand Fortresses at forty thousand feet,
Forty thousand Fortresses at forty thousand feet,
But they only take a teeny-weeny bomb.

We're flying Flying Fortresses at forty thousand feet,
Flying over Germany to give the Huns a treat,
We've bags and bags of ammo and a teeny weeny bomb
And we drop the bastard from so high we don't know where it's
gone.

We'll fly a Flying Fortress up to forty thousand feet.
The gunners think the fighters are a load of easy meat.
We've bags of ammunition and a teeny little bomb
And when we drop the son-of-a-bitch we don't know where it's
gone.

If we go down any lower we'll get mixed up with the Lancs
[repeat twice]
And we've only got a teeny little bomb.

CHORUS   *Glory Glory shall we drop it?*
                Glory Glory shall we drop it?
                Glory Glory shall we drop it?
                Shall we drop our teeny-weeny bomb?

They've lots of ammunition and lots of point five guns,
They've lots of ammunition and lots of point five guns,
They've lots of ammunition and lots of point five guns,
But they only take a teeny-weeny bomb.

They've bags of fighter cover and they've bags of armour plate,
They've bags of fighter cover and they've bags of armour plate,
They've bags of fighter cover and they've bags of armour plate,
But they only take a teeny-weeny bomb.

They get a gong from Congress when they've only done five ops,
They get a gong from Congress when they've only done five ops,
They get a gong from Congress when they've only done five ops,
But they only take a teeny-weeny bomb.

Four and twenty Hali's (or Lancs) go in at two thousand feet,
Four and twenty Hali's go in at two thousand feet,
Four and twenty Hali's go in at two thousand feet,
But they've all got a – BLOODY GREAT BOMB!

Editorial Note:
Mosquito Mk XVI: 4000 lb 'cookie' and a crew of two; 350 knots.
Flying Fortress: 2,000 lb bomb load; crew of eleven; 150 knots.

The Briefing

(Tune – Lili Marlene)

When you go to Briefing, the target gives you a fright,
Open up the throttles and leap into the night.
We've left the flarepath far behind.
It's cold up here, but we don't mind.
We're pressing on regardless for the Winco's DFC.

There go the flak bursts, target's burning bright.
There go the fighter flares, panic in the night.
We've left our home base far behind.
It's cold up here, but we don't mind.
We're pressing on regardless for the Winco's DFC.

You go to Hamburg and I'll go to Essen

(Tune – Loch Lomond)

You go to Hamburg and I'll go to Essen,
And I'll be a'weaving afore you,
But if you're a bit lax, you'll get the bloody axe,
And we'll meet in Duluft in the morning.

We are the Royal Air Force

(Tune – The Church is One Foundation)

We are the Royal Air Force,
No bloody good are we,
[What bloody fools are we,]
The only times you'll find us,
Are breakfast, lunch and tea.

But when it comes to pay-day
[And when the Great Call cometh]
We shout with all our might,
"Per Ardua ad Astra,"
Sod [Fuck] you Jack, I'm alright!

We are the Air Sea Rescue

We are the Air Sea Rescue,
No ruddy use are we,
The only time you'll see us
Is breakfast, lunch or tea,
And if you're in the 'oggin
By day or in the night,
Per Ardua Ad Astra,
Fuck you Jack, I'm all right.

Bless 'em All

Bless 'em all, Bless 'em all,
The long and the short and the tall,
Bless all the Sergeants and WO ones,
Bless all the Corporals and their bastard sons,
For we're saying 'goodbye' to them all,
As back to their barracks they crawl,
We'll get no promotion,
This side of the ocean,
So cheer up my lads, Bless 'em all.

They say there's a troopship just leaving Bombay,
Bound for Old Blighty's shore,
Heavily laden with time-expired men,
Bound for the land they adore.
There's many an Airman just finished his time,
There's many a bloke signing on,
But you'll get no promotion this side of the ocean,
So cheer up my lads, Bless 'em all.

They say there's a Whitley just leaving the Ruhr,
Bound for old Blighty's shore,
Heavily laden with terrified men,
Shit-scared and prone on the floor.
There's many a Junkers been shooting in lead
And many a Messerschmitt too,
They've fucked our hydraulics
And shot off our bollocks,
So what's a poor Airman to do?

Carry on! Carry on! Though our ammunition's all gone,
The Wop/AG has got frost-bite, the Bomb Aimer's sick,
The Navs at his table just twitching his prick,
So we're saying fuck-all to them all,
As up the CO's arsehole we crawl,
You'll get no promotion this side of the ocean,
So cheer up my lads, Bless 'em all!

504 Auxiliary Squadron

(Tune – Regimental March Warwickshire Regiment)

Oh Merry, Oh Merry, Oh Merry are we!
We are the 504 Auxiliary.
Fly high, fly low, wherever you go!
Auxiliary Airmen they never say, "No!"

We've plenty of Corporals and NCOs
What they got their stripes for the Lord only knows.
They stand on street corners they sing and they shout
They shout about things they know fuck-all about.

We've plenty of fitters and riggers too
Lounging about till the break wagon's due
And when there's a flap on they all stand and stare
While our pansy pilots take off in the air.

They sent the Auxiliary over to France
Gorblimey! Old Jerry he led us a dance.
He pinched our equipment and aeroplanes too
And left the Auxiliary with fuck-all to do!

Thanks for the Memory

Thanks for the memory
Of biplanes in the sky,
Of pilots who can't fly,
Of four hour trips,
Torpedoed ships,
Returning with a sigh.
How lovely it was.

D-Day Dodgers

(Tune – Lili Marlene)

We are the D-Day Dodgers,
Out in Italy.
Always on the vino, always on the spree.
Eighth Army shivers in their tanks,
We live in Rome among the Yanks.
We are the D-Day Dodgers in sunny Italy.

We landed at Salerno, a holiday with pay,
The Jerries brought the banners out and made us tea,
We all had girls, the beer was free,
To welcome the D-Day Dodgers in sunny Italy.

Naples and Casino were taken in our stride,
We didn't go to fight there, we just went for the ride,
Anzio and Sangro, they're just names,
We only went to look for dames.
We are the D-Day Dodgers in sunny Italy.

Dear Lady Astor, you think you know a lot,
Standing on a platform and talking bloody rot,
You're England's sweetheart and the pride,
We think your mouth's too fucking wide.
That's from your D-Day Dodgers in sunny Italy.

Look around the mountain in the mud and rain,
See the scattered crosses, some which have no name,
Heartbreak and toil and suffering gone,
The boys beneath them slumber on.
Those are your D-Day Dodgers,
Who stayed in Italy.

The Modern Meteorologist

(Parody of 'The Modern Major General' from 'The Pirates of Penzance')

I am the very model of a modern Meteorologist,
A scientific calling and one needing no apologist.
I diagnose the weather without any doubt or lingerin',
The forecast turns out well on days I haven't got my finger in.
I'm pally with St Swithin and Old Moore's an ancient friend of mine
J Pluvius, the weather clerk and Buchan often sends a line
And if it's necessary I'm delighted to inspire a
Correspondence with the shades of Ananias and Sapphira.
I explain my charts to callers in a useful terminology,
Of words that might mean anything, of doubtful etymology:
Houdini isn't in it, I'm that noted escapologist,
That equivocating casuist, the modern Meteorologist.

I keep the pilots well supplied with "gen" on visibility,
The customers are satisfied, our motto is civility.
I tell them what the weather's like from Yeovilton to Stornoway,
And answer silly questions till the telephone is worn away.
To please the plotting office Wren I read the anemometer,
And give her information, though I'd rather throw a bomb at her:
But the duty I like best of all my duties is the daily 'un,
Explaining things away with learned words sesquipedalian,
For when I get involved in conversation catechitical,
I obfuscate the questioner with answers most political.
The science doesn't matter, I'm a skilful escapologist
Who'll get away with anything, a modern Meteorologist.

In fact when I know what is meant by equigeopotential,
When I can speak to brass-hats in a manner consequential,
When I have learned to change a simple statement to a paragraph,
And tell unhesitatingly a wind-vane from a barograph:
When I can make Commander (F) believe my forecasts fictional
And carefully constructed with the help of rules predictional,
When I've become a walking encyclopaedia of weather lore,
I'll qualify to occupy that office on the nether floor,
When I can make a forecast read in terms still MORE ambiguous,
And base emphatic statements in synoptics quite exiguous,
Then I'll consider I've become that brilliant escapologist,
The pilot's guide and counsellor, the modern Meteorologist.

Arse-End Charlie

(Tune – Champagne Charlie)

Arse-end Charlie is me name,
Arse-end flying is me game,
There's no future flying up in front,
Unless you're a hero or silly cunt.

I like flying at the back,
I keep weaving when there's flak,
And when there's a fighter coming up my chuff,
Or if my engine sounds a wee bit duff.

My formation's pretty tight,
'Till Japan is out of sight.
I don't want to rise to fame,
So Arse-end Charlie I'll remain.

Ops In A Wimpey

(Tune – Waltzing Matilda)

Ops in a Wimpey,
Ops in a Wimpey,
Who'll come on Ops in a Wimpey with me?
And the Rear Gunner sang, as he loaded up his 303,
"Who'll come on Ops in a Wimpey with me?"

Ops In A Whitley

Ops in a Whitley,
Ops in a Whitley,
Who'll come on Ops in a Whitley with me?
And he sang as he laughed
         and pushed the throttles open,
Who'll come on Ops in a Whitley with me?

There's A Home For Batchy Airmen

(Tune – There's a Home for Little Children) Batchy = crazy.

There's a home for batchy airmen
Way out in the sunny Sudan.
The airmen are all batchy
And so is the fucking Old Man.

There's a home for crazy airmen down in the sunny Sudan,
Where every bugger's barmy including the fucking Old Man,
There's bags and bags of bullshit, saluting on the square,
And when we're not saluting, we're up in the fucking air.

Oh we're leaving Khartoum by the light of the moon,
We're flying by night and by day,
We've passed Kasfareet with fuck-all to eat,
'Cos we'e thrown all our rations away.

Chorus   *Shire, Shire, Somersetshire,*
        The Skipper looks on her with pride,
        But he'd have a blue fit,
        If he saw all the (any) shit,
        On the side of the Somersetshire.

There's bags and bags of bullshit
Saluting on the square,
And when we are not saluting,
We're up in the fucking air.

Now two long years I've been here
Among the shit and sand.
The sun has burned my eyeballs,
The sun has scorched my hand.

We're flying in the sunshine,
Saluting in the rain
And when we go from Khartoum,
We'll never come back again.

We're leaving Khartoum in the cattle saloon,
                              [by the light of the moon]
We're sailing by night and by day,
We've passed Kasfareet, we've got fuck-all to eat
'Cos we've given [thrown] our rations away.

This is my story, this is my song.
We've been in this Air Force too fucking long,
So roll out the *Nelson*, the *Rodney* and *Renown*,
You can't have the *Hood* 'cos the bastard's gone down.

Roll your own, what d'ya say?
Oh! We'll stuff all the SPs who come down our way.

It's foolish but it's fun

(Aircrew version of the popular 1940s song)

I'd love to fly an aeroplane,
A Spitfire or a Hurricane,
Then I'd try a bomber plane,
It's foolish but it's fun.

I'd love to be a Wop/AG,
And fly all over Germany,
And get shot up to buggery,
It's foolish but it's fun.

If it should ever come to pass,
That I should get my wings,
I'd fly all day and fly all night
And do such crazy things.

I'd fly the aircraft in steep banks,
Drop my bombs on British tanks
And shoot down all the bleedin' Yanks.
It's foolish but it's fun.

A Spitfire Story

Ain't feelin' quite so good today, I'm even off me beer!
Altho' they've given me ten days leave, I still feel kinda queer.
I've had a nasty shock you see, I've lost my biggest chum,
It happened just a week ago, and better men don't come.

My pal's a famous fighter ace, DSO and DFC,
His score of Jerry buses had just reached twenty-three.
Squadron Leader Brand, the finest bloke I've met,
Him and me was really pals, that makes you smile I'll bet.

Him a proper English gent, public school and Oxford Blue
And me a common Cockney bloke, just an AC2.
A Spitfire fighter pilot and his rigger, that was us
The bloke who did the scrapping and me what did his bus,

A "fighting team" he said we were, altho' he'd got three rings.
"Jimmy you're all right," he said, altho' he'd got the wings.
"You're the bloke that I depend on when I'm up there in a fight,
I can't shoot 'em down unless you fix my Spitfire right."

He was always kind and thoughtful, when my missus had a kid,
He sent a wire, a bunch of flowers, as well as fifteen quid.
I told him I was grateful, said I'd make it up to him,
He gave a crooked smile and said, "You owe me nothing, Jim.

I've got a pair of silver Wings, two medals on my chest,
My name's been in the papers, there's promotion and the rest.
I've got twenty-three swastikas painted on my petrol tank
For all these things it's blokes like you I've really got to thank."

The day he'd been to see the King to get his DSO
They 'ad a lovely party, all 'is friends and the CO.
But 'e got away for just a while to buy us drinks all round,
"You can't win medals in the sky with dud blokes on the ground."

'Killer' Brand they called him, the pilot of no Wing,
What a name to give a bloke who'd never harm a thing,
Except when he was chasing Huns; Blimey then he'd fight!
You see he'd lost his sister when Jerry came one night.

The girls were crazy after him, they chased him near and far,
Made his life a misery, just like a movie star.
Wouldn't have no truck with 'em, perhaps they thought him dumb,
If they did, he didn't worry, his best girl was his Mum.

A week ago last Monday, I won't forget that day,
It was cold wet and dreary, all the sky was grey.
They took off them twelve Spitfires on an early morning sweep,
Just like a hundred other days, I waved and said, "God keep".

I couldn't seem to settle down the time they was away,
I seemed to have a feeling this was goin' to be *his* day.
I waited on the airfield 'til I sighted them – and then,
One, two, three, four, five, six, seven, eight, nine, ten,

I quickly checked them over, but his crate it wasn't there.
I asked the other pilots if they'd seen him bale and where?
They'd seen him crashing down in flames, "Tony's gone we fear."
I ain't feeling quite so good today – I'm even off me beer!

Group HQ

Group Headquarters is such fun,
Bags of bumph but nowt gets done.
Acting ranks are just the thing,
Chasing up the odd half ring.
Seems to be the sport of many,
Though there really isn't any
Need for all these senior bods,
Wincos, Groupies, Oh Ye Gods!
Why have a so high ranking mob,
When a Clerk GD could do the job?

William Anderson Tibbles

An Old-Fashioned Hali

(Tune – Old-Fashioned Lady)

Just an old-fashioned Hali,
With old-fashioned ways,
With a fuselage tattered and torn.

Just an old-fashioned turret,
With old-fashioned guns,
That the gunners D.I. every morn.

When she's up she looks swell,
She can battle like hell,
As the people of Berlin will tell.

When she's way up on high,
She's the queen of the sky,
That old-fashioned Hali of mine.

An Old-Fashioned Wimpey

She's an old-fashioned Wimpey
With old-fashioned ways,
And a fuselage tattered and torn.

Two old-fashioned engines
Which never will run,
For the bearings are rusty and worn.

Oh, she drinks bags of petrol,
And sweet Casterol,
But there's one thing that makes her sublime.

She is so safe and sound,
For she won't leave the ground,
That Old-Fashioned Wimpey of mine!

Our Flight Sergeant

(Tune – John Brown's Body)

Our Flight Sergeant has a Crown upon his arm,
Our Flight Sergeant has a Crown upon his arm,
Our Flight Sergeant has a Crown upon his arm,
But the bastard thinks he's got it on his head.

Our Flight Sergeant fell from forty thousand feet
Our Flight Sergeant fell from forty thousand feet
Our Flight Sergeant fell from forty thousand feet
Now he ain't going to fly no more.

Glory, Glory, what a hell of a way to die,
Glory, Glory, what a hell of a way to die,
Glory, Glory, what a hell of a way to die,
Now he ain't going to fly no more.

They scraped him off the runway like a dollop of strawberry jam,
They scraped him off the runway like a dollop of strawberry jam,
They scraped him off the runway like a dollop of strawberry jam,
Now he ain't going to fly no more.

They wrapped him up in four by two and sent him off to Mum,
They wrapped him up in four by two and sent him off to Mum,
They wrapped him up in four by two and sent him off to Mum,
Now he ain't going to fly no more.

She put him on the mantelpiece amongst the souvenirs,
She put him on the mantelpiece amongst the souvenirs,
She put him on the mantelpiece amongst the souvenirs,
Now he ain't going to fly no more.

The Bloody Great Wheel

An Airman told me before he died,
I do not know if the bastard lied,
He had a wife with a cunt so wide,
She never could be satisfied.

[A blacksmith told me before he died,
And I've no reason to believe he lied,
That no matter how hard he tried,
His wife was never satisfied.]

So they built a prick of steel,
Two brass balls and a fucking great wheel,
Both the balls were filled with cream
And the whole fucking issue was driven by steam.

[So he built a prick of steel,
Fastened it to a bloody great wheel,
Nine feet long and stuffed with cream,
And the whole fucking issue was driven by steam].

[So he built a bloody great wheel,
Harnessed to it a prick of steel,
Two brass balls were filled with cream,
And the whole fucking issue was driven by steam].

Round and round went the fucking great wheel,
In and out went the prick of steel,
'Till at last the maiden cried,
"Enough! Enough! I'm satisfied!"

Now we come to the bitter [biter] bit,
There was no way [means] of stopping it.
She was split from arse to tit
And the whole fucking issue was covered in …

Sweet Violets, sweeter than all the roses,
Covered all over from arse to tit
Covered all over in – SHIT!

Shaibah Blues

(Tune – A Little Bit of Heaven)

A little piece of bullshit fell from the sky one day,
And it landed in the ocean three thousand miles away,
And when the Air Force found it, it looked so bloody bare,
They said, "That's what we're looking for,
                    we'll put our Air Force there."

So they sent out three Wimpeys and they sent out SHQ,
And then they put our Squadron there, right in the sodding blue,
To a place that's so remote and all you hear both night and day,
"Roll on that bloody boat!"

I've got those Shaibah Blues,
I'm fed up, I'm fucked up, I'm blue,
I have tried to learn the lingo but it really gets my goat,
The only thing that I can say is, "Roll on that fucking boat."

I've got those Shaibah Blues, Shaibah Blues,
I'm fed up, I'm fucked up, I'm blue."

Scapa Flow

Sure a little bit of dirt and shit fell out the sky one day,
And it landed in the hogwash not so many miles away,
And when the Navy found it sure it looked so bleak and bare,
They said 'suppose we leave it for a Naval Base up there'.
So they dotted it with battleships to make its lakes look grand,
And they crowded it with Matelots, the best in all the land:
Then they sprinkled it with rain and sleet and hail and bloody snow,
And when they had finished sure they called it SCAPA FLOW!

Mr Pupil and Mr Instructor

(Tune: Mr Mercer & Mr Crosby Mr Gallagher & Mr Sheen)

Oh, Mr Instructor, Oh, Mr Instructor,
Can you tell me how my flying's been assessed?
Though I spin out of control,
When I try half a flick roll,
A Guy can do no better than his best.

Oh, Mr Pupil, Oh, Mr Pupil,
Say, your best is not quite good enough for me.
You'll enjoy much better health
In a thing that rolls itself.
In a Martlet, Mr Instructor?
In a Corvette, Mr P.

Oh, Mr Instructor, Oh, Mr Instructor,
All the other boys are hogging it today
And I wanted to find out
What the noise is all about,
Are these Harvard aircraft really here to stay?

Oh, Mr Pupil. Yes, Mr Instructor?
Though you other boys had Harts taped to a "Tee",
In the skyways you will play
In this same abandoned way.
Straight and level Mr Instructor?
Upward Charlies, Mr P.

Oh, Mr Instructor. Yes, Mr Pupil?
I've been reading in the flying magazines,
When an aircraft starts to spin
Auto-rotation will set in.
Can you tell me what this language really means?

Oh Mr Pupil. Yes, Mr Instructor?
When your aircraft speed begins to dwindle rapidly,
If that aircraft starts to yaw,
You're going to wind up on the floor.
How too, too, thrilling, Mr Instructor.
It's devastating Mr P.

Oh, Mr Instructor. Yes, Mr Pupil?
The man who teaches airmanship tells me
That the centrifugal force
Is enough to kill a horse
If you fool around at more than seven "G".

Oh, Mr Pupil. Yes, Mr Instructor?
Once a Guy who thought he knew a thing or three
Pulled the stick back at full power
At three hundred miles an hour.
Did he get his Wings Mr Instructor?
On his shoulders, Mr P.

Oh, Mr Instructor. Yes, Mr Pupil?
These precautionary landings are a bore.
Now I'm holding off at last,
Only three feet from the grass,
Can you tell me what that horn is sounding for?

Oh, Mr Pupil. Yes, Mr Instructor?
There's a handle on the left side don't you see,
If that handle's not pressed down,
You'll land too close to the ground,
A three-pointer, Mr Instructor?
On your belly, Mr P.

Oh, Mr Instructor. Yes, Mr Pupil?
Is it true that flying's ancient as the hills
And the first galoot who flew
Way up in the skies so blue
Thought that 50 MPH was packed with thrills?

Oh, Mr Pupil, oh, Mr Pupil,
Nowadays we have our airscrews made VP,
With a boost of forty-eight
When the throttle's through the gate.
That's going places Mr Instructor.
Mr P you're telling me.

Oh, Mr Instructor. Yes, Mr Pupil?
It's a thousand pounds a U-boat they tell me,
When you see that U-boat's wake,
Why, it's just a piece of cake.
You just drop your bombs and bog off home to tea.

Oh, Mr Pupil, oh, Mr Pupil,
A Marine dive-bombed a U-boat out at sea,
He did three-oh-nine straight down,
In five minutes he came round.
In the water, Mr Instructor?
In the U-boat, Mr P.

Anti-War Panacea

If the Polish financier Koc
Met the Czechoslovakian Kundt,
It would strengthen the Latvian bloc
It would stiffen the Popular Front.

Uniting the part with the whole,
How fertile the issue would be,
For the Czech would lie down with the Pole
And Berlin be, of course, on the spree.

The Marital powers would achieve
With naval disarmament peace:
Which wouldn't be hard to conceive
From the seamen this act would release.

And the press, of the Chamberlain school
Would score a political hit
With headlines of "Communist Tool
Widens Czechoslovakian split."

It would strengthen the Latvian bloc,
If would stiffen the Popular Front,
If the Polish financier Koc,
Met the Czechoslovakian Kundt.

Bawdy Ballads

Fifty-One Squadron

Fifty-One Squadron, Fifty-One men,
Fly over Germany and fly back again.
Fifty-One Squadron, Fifty-One men,
They're not there to fight the foe,
You might think so, but Oh Dear, No.
They're just there to have a go
And put a bit of action in the Goering show.

They fly in Whitleys, big and black,
And all think they're the ones who're coming back,
Fifty-One Squadron, Fifty-One men,
They fly by night-time, they fly by day,
But when there's a clamp on then
It's boys come out to play.
Fifty-One Squadron, Fifty-One men.

I Haven't Seen Old Hitler

I haven't seen old Hitler for a hell of a time,
I haven't seen old Hitler for a hell of a time,
I went to France to see what he was doin'.
When I got there the fucking place was ruined,
I haven't seen old Hitler for a hell of a time,
He must have been buggered by a mine,
But if he's the leader of the Deutchland breeder,
Fuck him, he's no cousin of mine,
No cousin of mine, no cousin of mine.
I've got dozens of every kind,
England, Ireland, Scotland, Wales,
Russia, Prussia and Jerusalem,
Africa, America and Germany all along the line,
But if he's the leader of the Deutchland breeder,
Fuck him, he's no cousin of mine.

Old King Cole

Old King Cole was a Merry Old Soul,
And a Merry Old Soul was he,
He called for his kites in the middle of the night,
And he called for his Pilots three.

Every Pilot was a very fine type [chap]
and a very fine chap was he.
"I don't give two fucks," said the Pilot,
For Merry, Merry men are we,
There's none so fair as can compare,
With the lads of "EIGHTY-THREE".

Old King Cole was a Merry Old Soul,
And a Merry Old Soul was he,
He called for his kites in the middle of the night,
And he called for his Navigators three.

Every Navigator was a very fine chap and a very fine chap was he.
"Fifteen miles off course," said the Navigator,
"I don't give two fucks," said the Pilot,
For Merry, Merry men are we,
There's none so fair as can compare,
With the lads of "CONINGSBY".

Old King Cole was a Merry Old Soul,
And a Merry Old Soul was he,
He called for his kites in the middle of the night,
And he called for his Flight Engineers three.

Every Engineer was a very fine chap and a very fine chap was he.
"I want four pounds of boost," said the Engineer,
"Fifteen miles off course," said the Navigator,
"I don't give two fucks," said the Pilot,
For Merry, Merry men are we,
There's none so fair as can compare,
With the lads of "ONE-O-THREE".

Old King Cole was a Merry Old Soul,
And a Merry Old Soul was he,
He called for his kites in the middle of the night,
And he called for his Bomb Aimers three.

Every Bomb Aimer was a very fine chap
and a very fine chap was he.
"Left, right, left, left, left," said the Bomb Aimer,
"I want four pounds of boost," said the Engineer,
"Fifteen miles off course," said the Navigator,
"I don't give two fucks," said the Pilot,
For Merry, Merry men are we,
There's none so fair as can compare,
With the lads from "WICKENBY".

Old King Cole was a Merry Old Soul,
And a Merry Old Soul was he,
He called for his kites in the middle of the night,
And he called for his Wireless Ops three.

Every Wireless Op was a very fine chap
and a very fine chap was he.
"Dah Diddly Dah Diddly Dah," said the Wireless Op,
"Left, right, left, left, left," said the Bomb Aimer,
"I want four pounds of boost," said the Engineer,
"Fifteen miles off course," said the Navigator,
"I don't give two fucks," said the Pilot,
For Merry, Merry men are we,
There's none so fair as can compare,
With the lads of the ...

Old King Cole was a Merry Old Soul,
And a Merry Old Soul was he,
He called for his kites in the middle of the night,
And he called for his Mid-Uppers three.

Every Mid-Upper was a very fine chap
and a very fine chap was he.
"Corkscrew Port Like Hell," said the Mid-Upper,
OR "Rat A Tat A Tat A Tat A Tat" said the Mid-Upper,
"Dah Diddly Dah Diddly Dah," said the Wireless Op,
"Left, right, left, left, left," said the Bomb Aimer,
"I want four pounds of boost," said the Engineer.
"Fifteen miles off course," said the Navigator,
"I don't give two fucks," said the Pilot,
For Merry, Merry men are we,
There's none so fair as can compare with the lads of the ...

Old King Cole was a Merry Old Soul,
And a Merry Old Soul was he,
He called for his kites in the middle of the night,
And he called for his Rear Gunners three.

Every Rear Gunner was a very fine type
and a very fine type was he.
"Bloody Hell! It's cold!" said the Rear Gunner,
"Rat A Tat A Tat A Tat A Tat" said the Mid-Upper,
"Dah Diddly Dah Diddly Dah," said the Wireless Op,
"Left, right, steady, steady, steady," said the Bomb Aimer,
"I want four pounds of boost," said the Engineer.
"Bang on course," said the Navigator,
"I don't give two fucks," said the Pilot,
For Merry, Merry men are we,
There's none so fair as can compare,
With the lads of the ...

REPEAT SLOWLY   *There's none so fair as can compare*
                    With the Mates who flew with me.

Old King Cole #2

In the OTC, way back in the late 1930s, we sang this version.

Old King Cole was a Merry Old Soul,
And a Merry Old Soul was he,
He called for his ?...? in the middle of the night,
And he called for his Sergeants three.

Every Sergeant was a very fine chap and a very fine chap was he.
"Move to the right in fours," said the Sergeant,
"Left .., left .., left, right, left," said the Corporal,
For Merry, Merry men are we,
There's none so fair as can compare with the boys of the OTC.

Old King Cole #3

Old King Cole was a Merry Old Soul
And a merry old soul was he.
He called for his wife in the middle of the night
And he called for his fiddlers three.
Now every fiddler had a very fine fiddle
And a very fine fiddle had he.
"Fiddle diddle dee diddle dee," said the fiddlers,
"What merry merry men are we,
There's none so fair as can compare
With the boys of the RFC."

Old King Cole was a Merry Old Soul
And a merry old soul was he.
He called for his wife in the middle of the night
And he called for his tailors three.
Now every tailor had a very fine needle
And a very fine needle had he.
"Stick in, in and out, in and out," said the tailors,
"Fiddle diddle dee diddle dee," said the fiddlers,
"What merry merry men are we,
There's none so fair as can compare
With the boys of the RFC."

Old King Cole was a Merry Old Soul
And a merry old soul was he.
He called for his wife in the middle of the night
And he called for his jugglers three.
Now every juggler had two very fine balls
And two very fine balls had he.
"Throw your balls in the air," said the jugglers,
"Stick in, in and out, in and out," said the tailors,
"Fiddle diddle dee diddle dee," said the fiddlers,
"What merry merry men are we,
There's none so fair as can compare
With the boys of the RFC."

How Ashamed I Was

I touched her on the toe, how ashamed I was,
I touched her on the toe, how ashamed I was,
I touched her on the toe, she said, "You're mighty slow,"
Lord God Almighty how ashamed I was.

I touched her on the knee, how ashamed I was,
I touched her on the knee, how ashamed I was,
I touched her on the knee, she said, "You're mighty free,"
Lord God Almighty how ashamed I was.

[He put his hand upon my knee,
I said, "Young man, you're getting very free,
With your hand, with your h-a-n-d, your hand".] etc

I touched her on the thigh, how ashamed I was,
I touched her on the thigh, how ashamed I was,
I touched her on the thigh, she said, "You're getting high,"
Lord God Almighty how ashamed I was.

I touched her on her twat, how ashamed I was,
I touched her on her twat, how ashamed I was,
I touched her on her twat, she said, "You're getting hot,"
Lord God Almighty how ashamed I was.

[He put his hand upon my quim,
I said, "Young man, you'd better whip it in,
With your hand, with your h-a-n-d, your hand".]

And when I put it in, how ashamed I was,
And when I put it in, how ashamed I was,
And when I put it in, she said, "You're mighty thin,"
Lord God Almighty how ashamed I was.

And when I had come, how ashamed I was,
And when I had come, how ashamed I was,
And when I had come, she said, "You're up my bum,"
Lord God Almighty how ashamed I was.

She had to go and Lose it at the Astor

Favourite of Wingco Joe Skinner (Late President of Air Gunners Assn)

Her Mother said: "Minnie, you're all dressed up in your finery, your very best clothes and you look beautiful, you're gorgeous, you're alluring, you look swell Baby. And now, Minnie, I want you to remember everything I've always told you, and above all I want you to be very, very, careful."

But she had to go and lose it at the Astor,
She didn't take her Mother's good advice,
Now there are not so many girls today who have one,
And she'd never let it go for any price.

They searched the place from Penthouse to the cellar,
In every room and underneath each bed,
Once they thought they saw it lying on a pillow,
But they found it belonged to someone else instead.

But she had to go and lose it at the Astor,
She didn't know exactly who to blame,
And she couldn't say just how or when she lost it,
She only knew she had it when she came.

They questioned all the bell boys and the porters,
The test appears to be the girls deny,
And the doorman acted quite suspicious,
But he coyly said, "It wasn't I."

But she had to go and lose it at the Astor,
It nearly killed her Mother and her Dad,
Now they felt as bad about the thing as she did,
After all, it was the only one she had!

They'd just about completed all their searching,
When the chauffeur walked up with it in his hand,
All they did was stand and gape,
There was Minnie's sable cape,
And she thought she'd lost it at the Astor.

We are the Heavy Bombers

(Tune John Brown's Body)

We are the heavy bombers, we try to do our bit,
We fly through concentrations of flak and cloud and shit,
And when we drop our cargoes, we do not give a damn,
The eggs may miss the goods yard, but they eff-up poor old Ham.

CHORUS   *Ain't the Airforce effing awful,*
               Ain't the Airforce effing awful,
               Ain't the Airforce effing awful,
               And we made an effing landfall in the Firth of effing
Forth.

And when in adverse weather the winds are all to Hell,
The Navigator's ballsed up, the wireless ballsed as well,
We think of all the Popsies we've known in days gone by,
And curse the silly effers who taught us how to fly.

They sent us off to Egypt, a very pleasant land,
Where miles and miles of sweet eff-all are covered up with sand,
And when we got to Cairo, the girls were heard to say,
"There ain't no hope for us dears, Thirty-seven's come to stay."

And when you get to Hades, it's just like SHQ,
With lots and lots of stooges sitting around with eff-all else to do,
They ask you for your flimsies and your pass and target maps,
You take the ruddy issue and you stuff them down their traps.

We had been flying all day long at a hundred effing feet,
The weather effing awful, effing rain and effing sleet,
The compass it was swinging effing South and effing North,
But we made an effing landfall in the Firth of effing Forth.

We joined the effing Airforce 'cos we thought it effing right,
But we don't care if we effing fly or if we effing fight,
But what we do object to are those effing ops-room twats,
Who sit there sewing stripes on at a rate of effing knots.

Belting Down the Runway

Belting down the runway
On Aquaba's marshy shores,
With bags and bags of bullshit
And bags of jungle sores,
Second dicky's charping,
He's just come for the ride,
When we get back from out of this mess,
We'll put this fucking kite U/S.
We're round the fucking corner,
We're round the fucking bend.

Hard Cider

'Neath the shade of the old apple tree,
As I looked 'tween her legs I could see
A little brown spot and she called it her twat,
But it looked like a birds' nest to me.

I asked her how deep it could be,
She said, "Shove in your tool and you'll see,"
So I shoved in my gun and I shot a home run,
'Neath the shade of the old apple tree.

Then I asked her how much it would be,
She said, "To you, Sir, it's free."
So I shoved it in tight and stayed there all night,
'Neath the shade of the old apple tree.
She said, "If you'll be true,
You can have a suck too!
In the shade of the old apple tree."

North Atlantic Squadron

The NCOs are a bunch of sluts,
The LACs got all the guts
The WDs get all the nuts
In the North Atlantic Squadron.

CHORUS: *Away, away, with fife and drum,*
Here we come full of rum,
Looking for women who peddle their bum,
In the North Atlantic Squadron.

Thirty days we're out to sea,
The Captain took to buggery,
The Cabin Boy was his only joy,
In the North Atlantic Squadron.

For forty days and forty nights
We sailed the broad Atlantic,
And never to pass a piece of cunt,
It nearly drove us frantic.

The Captain had a Cabin Boy,
Pernicious little nipper,
He filled his arse with ground-up glass
And circumcised the Skipper.

The Captain loved the Cabin Boy,
He loved him like a brother,
And every night between the sheets
They cornholed one another.

He also had another boy
A tricky little nipper,
He filled his bum with bubble gum
And vulcanised the Skipper.

The cook she ran about the deck
The Captain he pursued her,
He caught her on the afterdeck
The dirty bastard screwed her.

The Second Mate did masturbate,
No cock was higher or wider,
They cut off his cock upon a rock,
For pissing in the cider.

In days of old when knights were bold
And women weren't particular,
They lined them up against the wall
And fucked them perpendicular.

In days of old when men were bold
And Johnnies weren't invented,
They wrapped a sock around their cock
And babies were prevented.

The firemen they fight the fire.
They never, never, seem to tire
Of filling their arseholes and pulling their wire
In the North Atlantic Squadron.

The wireless boys they fly so high,
I wish to Christ that they would die,
Their did-dah-dits give us the shits
In the North Atlantic Squadron.

The Officers they know fuck-all,
As up the CO's arse they crawl,
But what does it get them but sweet fuck-all
In the North Atlantc Squadron.

And when we get to Montreal
We'll fuck the women short and tall
For you don't use your hand in the Coastal Command
In the North Atlantic Squadron.

We're off, we're off to Montreal
We'll fuck the women, we'll fuck them all,
We'll pickle their cherries in alcohol
On the North Atlantic Squadron.

There was a whore from Montreal,
She spread her legs from wall to wall,
But all she got was sweet fuck-all
From the North Atlantic Squadron.

There was a whore from Singapore,
Hung upside down inside a door,
And she was left, split, worn and sore
By the North Atlantic Squadron.

Large Balls

Miss Jones was walking down the street,
When a young fella she happened to meet,
Who was giving the girls a helluva treat
By twisting and turning his balls.

Chorus: *For they were large balls, large balls,*
             Twice as heavy as lead.
             With a dextrous twist of his muscular wrist
             He threw them right over his head.

A policeman to the scene was brought
He said, "I'll have to take you to Court
'Cos it's certain that nobody ought
To be twisting and turning his balls."

The prisoner standing in the dock
Gave the Judge a helluva shock
By insisting on showing the Jury his cock
And twisting and turning his balls.

The Judge he said, "The case is clear,
The fine will be a barrel of beer
For any young bugger who comes in here
Twisting and turning his balls."

The Youngest Child

She lay nude between the sheets
And I beside her lay:
And she was soft and round and chubby,
Under my hand uprose her bubby.

My hand beneath her waist did stroke,
Her tip-tops itched and tingled,
I clambered up, began to poke,
And our juices intermingled.

"Pull out! Pull out!" the fair one cried,
"Before I swell with trouble."
I did and on her snow-white breast
My come did froth and bubble.

I gazed into her frightened eyes,
And with a leery curse,
"This is the youngest child," I said,
"That you will ever nurse."

She picked it up with one fair hand,
And with a shocked, "Oh La!"
She threw the load into my face,
Saying, "Child, go kiss your Pa!"

A Little Bit

She likes a little bit in the morning,
She likes a little bit in the afternoon,
She likes a little bit with her tea,
When she's listening to the BBC.

She likes a little bit in the evening,
When the stars are shining bright,
She likes to take a little bit up to bed
Just in case she'd like a little bit in the night.

Baby Carriage

Around her leg she wore a purple garter,
She wore it in the Springtime and in the merry month of May,
And if you ask her why the hell she wore it,
She wore it for an Airman who was far, far, away.

CHORUS   *Far away, far away,*
                   She wore it for an Airman
                   Who was far, far, away.

Around the park she pushed a baby carriage,
She pushed it in the Springtime and in the merry month of May,
And if you asked her why the hell she pushed it,
She pushed it for an Airman who was far, far, away.

Behind the door her Father kept a shot gun,
He kept it in the Springtime and in the merry month of May,
And if you asked him why the Hell he kept it,
He kept it for an Airman who was far, far, away.

And in the gun he kept a silver bullet,
He kept it in the Springtime and in the merry month of May,
And if you asked him why the Hell he kept it,
He kept it for an Airman who was far, far, away.

Upon the grave she put a bunch of flowers,
She placed it in the Springtime and in the merry month of May,
And if you asked her why the hell she placed it,
She placed it for an Airman who was SIX FEET DOWN.

Nellie 'Awkins

I first met Nellie 'Awkins dahn the Ole Kent Road.
Er drawers were 'angin' dahn,
'Cos she'd been wiv Charlie Brahn.
I pressed a filthy tanner in 'er filthy bleedin' 'and,
'Cos she were a low dahn whore.

She wore no blouses
An' I wore no trouses
An' she wore no underclothes
An' when she caressed me
She damn near undressed me.
It's a thrill that no one knows.

I went to the doctor:
'E said, "Where did you block 'er?"
I said, "Dahn where the green grass grows."
'E said, quick as a twinkle,
"The pimple on yer winkle
Will be bigger than a red, red rose".

On Monday I touched her on the ankle

(Tune: On Sunday I walk out with a Soldier)

On Monday I touched her on the ankle,
On Tuesday I touched her on the knee,
On Wednesday, success, I lifted up her dress,
On Thursday she took me home to tea ... Gawd Blimey!

On Friday I put my hand upon it.
On Saturday she gave my balls a tweak,
And on Sunday after supper, I stuffed the whole thing up her
And now I'm paying ten and six a week!

Archibald Clare or the Jugulaire

There was a young man named Archibald Clare
And he was very populaire,
For he was a famous jugulaire
And used to play with his balls.

CHORUS   *For they were large balls,*
                 Balls as heavy as lead.
                 He gave them a flick
                 With the end of his prick
                 And swung them right over his head.

As he was walking down the street,
Little Miss Brown he chanced to meet,
Walking along with a dog at her feet,
As he twisted and turned his balls.

As he was swinging them round and round,
Down they came with a hell of a bound,
Right on top of the faithful hound,
Who was watching him play with his balls.

Now Little Miss Brown was overwrought
And swore she'd take the case to Court,
For in her opinion no man ought
To be twirling and twisting his balls.

They took him to a Magistrate,
Who put him in a cell in State
And left him there to meditate
On how to play with his balls.

And when they took the case to Court,
The Lawyer of the lady sought
To prove that Archibald didn't ought
To twist and twirl his balls.

The Jury said 'twas a bloody disgrace,
Exposing yourself in a public place,
Wagging your tool in a lady's face
And twisting and twirling your balls.

The Judge and Jury couldn't agree
And the Judge he said, "It's plain to see
And really and truly I cannot see
Why a man shouldn't play with his balls."

Then Archibald gave the Court a shock,
Bold as brass he left the Dock,
Swinging his balls around his cock,
Twirling and twisting his balls.

And this is the moral of this song,
If you play with your balls you can't go wrong,
So bang your balls against a gong
And twiddle and play with your balls.

Katukarunda

(Tune – Blaze Away)

Insanitary bogs, thieving wogs, got no time for "A" boys,
It's no ruddy wonder that Katukarunda has such a lousy smell,
With lizards and vipers and festering green stripers
And negative booze as well.
Go down to dispersal in whites washed in Persil
Through clouds of dust and sand,
Soon you're all gritty and dirty and shitty,
Chuck in your ruddy hand.

If you really want a tossed out jade,
You've got to join the shiny-arsed brigade.
If you're fond of whisky and gin and lime,
At Katukarunda you've had your time.
Shave off Katukarunda's wingless goons.

Little Angeline

(Various versions semi-merged)

She was sweet sixteen, Little Angeline,
Pure and innocent she'd always been,
[Always dancing on the village green]
Never had a thrill and a virgin still,
Poor Little Angeline.

At the village fair the Squire was there,
Masturbating in the middle of the square,
And his tool was raw whene'er he saw
Poor Little Angeline.

Now the village Squire had a low desire,
To be the biggest bastard in the whole damned Shire.
He had set his heart on the vital part
Of Poor Little Angeline.

As she raised her skirt to avoid the dirt,
Stepping through the puddle of the Squire's last squirt,
He chanced to see the comely [dainty] knee
Of poor Little Angeline.

He lifted his hat and said, "Your cat
Has been run over and it's been crushed quite flat,
My car is in the square, can I take you anywhere?"
Poor Little Angeline!

Now the dirty turd should have got the bird,
But instead she followed him without a word.
As they drove away, you could hear the people say,
"Poor Little Angeline."

They hadn't gone far, when he stopped the car
And took her into a low-down bar,
Where he filled her with gin to tempt her into sin,
Poor Little Angeline.

When he'd oiled her well he took her to a dell,
And decided to give her bloody fucking hell,
And try his luck with a lay-down fuck, on
Poor Little Angeline.

She cried out, "Rape!" when he raised her cape,
Poor little girlie there was no escape,
It was time someone came to save the name
Of Poor Little Angeline.

Now the tale is told of a Blacksmith bold,
Who'd loved Little Angeline for years untold,
And he vowed to be true, whatever they might do,
[He was handsome, true, and virile too,]
To Poor Little Angeline.

But sad to say that self-same day,
He'd been put in prison for years to stay,
For coming in his pants at the village dance,
With Poor Little Angeline.

Now the Blacksmith's cell overlooked the dell,
Where the Squire was giving Little Angeline hell,
And looking through the bars, he recognised the arse,
[As they reached the grass, he saw the arse,]
Of his Poor Little Angeline.

When he saw them start, he blew a fart,
And the walls of the prison simply fell apart,
And he ran like shit lest the squire should split
Poor Little Angeline.

When he got to the spot and saw what was what,
He tied the villain's cock in a grannie knot,
And as he writhed on his guts, he was kicked in the nuts
By Poor Little Angeline.

"Oh Blacksmith true, I love you true I do,
I can see by your trousers that you love me too,
Since I'm undressed come and do your best,"
Cried Poor Little Angeline.

Now it won't take long to complete my song,
'Cos the hero had a cock a full foot long,
And his phallic charm was as brawny as his arm,
HAPPY HAPPY LITTLE ANGELINE!

Poor Blind Nell

The sun shone on the village green,
It shone on poor blind Nell,
But did she see the sun that shone?
Did she fuckin' 'ell!

A Sailor to the village came,
The Captain of a lugger.
He captivated Poor Blind Nell,
The dirty, lousy bugger.

One night he slept with Poor Blind Nell:
He knew it wasn't lawful
And though her tits were very sweet,
Her feet smelt fuckin' awful.

He took the girl out on a punt
And to the seat he lashed 'er.
Then lacerated Poor Nell's cunt,
The dirty, lousy bastard.

And when he went to sea again,
He sent her books and parcels,
But did he write and thank Poor Nell?
Did he fuckin' arseholes!

The Bastard King of England

The minstrels sing of an ancient King,
Who lived long years ago,
He ruled his land with an iron hand,
And his ways were mean and low.
He was very fond of hunting within the Royal Wood,
He was very fond of apple pie and pulling the Royal Pud,
He was fat and forty and full of fleas,
And the Royal Tool hung down to his knees.
        Cheers for the Bastard King of England!

Now the Queen of Spain was an amorous dame,
An amorous dame was she,
She loved to fool with the Royal Tool
Of the King across the sea.
So she sent a Royal Message by a Royal Messenger,
To ask the King to come and spend a month in bed with her.
        Fun for the Bastard King of England!

Now Philip of France he shat his pants
When this news to him was brought,
He said, "She loves my rival,
Just because my tool is short."
So he sent the Count of Zipitizap
To give the Queen a dose of clap,
        Meant for the Bastard King of England!

When the news of this foul deed was brought
To England's Ancient Halls,
The King he swore by the Royal Whore
To have King Philip's balls.
So he offered half his Kingdom and a fuck at Queen Citance,
To the Royal, Loyal son-of-a-bitch who would bugger the King of
France.
        Good for the Bastard King of England!

So the Noble Duke of Sussex,
He galloped across to France,
He swore he was a Nancy, so
The King took down his pants.
Then he fastened a thong round the Royal Prong,
Mounted his horse and galloped along,
   Back to the Bastard King of England.

Now all the whores of London were lined up on the walls,
When told to shout for the Bastard King, the harlots shouted,
"Balls!"
And the King threw up his breakfast and grovelled on the floor,
For in the ride, the Frenchman's pride
Had stretched a yard or more.
So Philip of France usurped the Throne,
His sceptre was the Royal Bone.
   The end of the Bastard King of England!

Mr Codfish And Mr Sole

(Tune: The Church's One Foundation)

Good morning Mr Codfish, good morning Mr Sole,
I tried to fuck your daughter, I couldn't find 'er 'ole.
At last I found 'er 'ole, Sir, just beneath 'er 'and,
But give me all the world, Sir, I couldn't raise a stand.

At last I got a stand, Sir, very long and very thin,
But give me all the world, Sir, I couldn't pop it in.
At last I popped it in, Sir, and waggled it about,
But give me all the world, Sir, I couldn't get it out.

At last I got it out, Sir, all spunky and raw,
But give me all the world, Sir, I'll fuck that girl no more.
Oh yes I've learned my lesson that women are no good,
So give me all the world, Sir, I'll pull my fucking pud.

I got it out at last, Sir, 'twas hot and red and numb,
God-damn it Mr Codfish, I had it up her bum!

The Mayor of Bayswater's Daughter

(Tune – The Ash Grove)

The Mayor of Bayswater's
Got a whore for a daughter
And the hairs on her Dickey-di-do
Hang down to her knees.

CHORUS   *One black one, one white one*
                And one with a bit of shite on.
                And the hairs on her dickey-di-do
                Hung down to her knees.

She lived in a lighthouse,
That stank like a fucking shitehouse...

I know 'cos I've seen 'em
I've been up and in between 'em ...

I've stroked 'em, I've poked 'em,
I've even rolled 'em up and smoked 'em ...

And if I should court her
I'd have to cut 'em shorter ...

She lives on a mountain
And pisses like a bloody fountain ...

She went to the 'Varsity
And there she lost her bleedin' charstity ...

She married a stoker,
With a prick like a bloody poker ...

She left him for an Italian,
With balls like a fucking stallion ...

Bollocky Bill the Sailor

"Who's that knocking at my door
Who's that knocking at my door
Who's that knocking at my door?"
Said the fair young maiden.

"It's only me from over the sea," said Bollocky Bill the Sailor.

Maiden: *"I'll come down and let you in,*
                I'll come down and let you in,
                I'll come down and let you in".

Bill: "And where am I going to sleep tonight?"

Maiden: "You may sleep upon the mat." (THRICE)

Bill: "Oh! Bugger the mat, I can't sleep on that!" (ONCE)

Maiden: "You can sleep between my thighs." (etc)

Bill: "What have you got between your thighs?"

Maiden: "I've got a pin cushion."

Bill: "I've got a pin, I will stick it."

Maiden: "But what if there should be a child?"

Bill: "Strangle the bastard as soon as it's born."

Maiden: "But what about the Police Force?"

Bill: "Bugger the Police and fuck the Force."

Maiden: "But what if there should be an Inquest?"

Bill: "Stuff the Inquest up your arse."

Maiden: "When shall I see you again?"

Bill: "Never no more you fucking old whore."

Blinded by Shit

There was an old lady who lived down our street:
She got constipation through too much to eat,
She took Beecham's pills on Saturday night,
And quickly she found that she wanted to shite.

CHORUS: *Too-ra-la, too-ra-lay,*
             Oh a rolling stone gathers no moss, so they say,
             Too-ra-la, too-ra-lay,
             It's a bloody fine song, but it's all about shit.

She went to the window and stuck out her arse,
At the moment a night-watchman happened to pass.
He heard a strange noise as he gazed up on high,
Then a bloody great turd hit him straight in the eye.

He looked to the North, he looked to the South
And a bloody great lump landed right in his mouth.
He looked to the East, he looked to the West,
As a further consignment arrived on his chest.

The next time you walk over Westminster Bridge,
Look out for an old man asleep on the edge,
His chest bears a placard and on it is writ:
"Be kind to an old man who's blinded by shit!"

Bloody Hell

This bloody town's a bloody cuss,
No bloody trains, no bloody bus,
And no one cares for bloody us.

CHORUS: *Bloody Shrimpton-Bassett (or wherever)*
         The bloody roads are bloody bad,
         The bloody folk are bloody mad,
         They'd make the brightest bloody sad.

All bloody clouds and bloody rains,
No bloody curbs, no bloody drains,
The Council's got no bloody brains.

Everything's so bloody dear,
A bloody bob for bloody beer,
And is it good? No bloody fear!

The bloody films are bloody old,
The bloody seats are bloody cold,
You can't get in for bloody gold!

No bloody sport, no bloody games,
No bloody fun: the bloody dames
Won't even give their bloody names!

The bloody dances make you smile,
The bloody band is bloody vile,
It only cramps your bloody style.

Best bloody place is bloody bed,
With bloody ice on bloody head,
You might as well be bloody dead!

The bloody baths are bloody cold,
The bloody news is bloody old,
To tell the truth is bloody bold.

The bloody pub's a bloody scream,
It's comfort's just a bloody dream,
It's bloody – that's just what I mean!

Brian Boru *(Tune – Too-ra-la too-ra-la too-ra-la-lay)*

CHORUS   *Hi g'lee, hi g'light, It's a bloody fine song,*
                I could sing it all night!

Now talking of fucking, well fucking's all right,
I once fucked a girl forty times in a night,
And each time I fucked her I shot her a quart,
If you don't call that fucking, you fucking well ought.

Now old Mrs Riley, she had a dun cow,
To milk that brown beastie she didn't know how,
She pulled on its tale instead of its tit
And poor Mother Riley got covered in shit.

Young Mary McGuire was a whore of renown.
The tracks of her arse were all over town.
Her tariff was fourpence, she never charged higher,
Fair fuck was the watchword of Mary McGuire.

Now Barny O'Flynn was a lad you should meet,
He'd clap from his head to the soles of his feet.
A globule of mercury hung from his chin,
"Begob oi am rotten," said Barny O'Flynn.

Young Brian Boru was a fine sort of lad,
There wasn't a stricture that he hadn't had.
And when he made water 'twas orange and blue,
"'Tis the old Oirish colours," said Brian Boru.

A policeman was walking one day on his beat,
When he heard a commotion way down on the street,
He turned round the corner and looked up on high,
And a can of hot shit hit him right in the eye.

He looked to the East and he looked to the West,
And another great turd hit him right on the chest.
He looked to the North and he looked to the South,
And a fucking great lump hit him right in the mouth.

That policeman was angry, that policeman was sore,
He called Mrs Riley a clap-ridden whore,
And now at the end of our street does he sit,
With a card round his neck saying, "Blinded by shit!"

Come on Boys

Come on boys, drinks all around, let's have a jolly good supper,
One man in bed with another man's wife is a fool if he doesn't ...

Send his boys to school, send his boys to school,
Before he's learned his ABC, he's playing with his ...

Mrs Murphy had two rabbits, one of them a buck,
She put them in a rabbit hutch to see if they would ...

Rule Britannia, two monkeys up a stick,
One put a finger where he should have put his ...

P stands for pudding, R stands for rice,
C stands for something else, it's naughty but it's ...

Blackpool is the place for me, there's fishing and there's rock,
I never use my fishing rod, I always use my ...

Pretty little finger, so slender and so slim,
I can get all five of them inside my girl-friend's ...

Pockets are so useful when you're out of luck,
Do not spend your last three ha'pence on a damned good ...

Turkish baths and manicure to make yourelf look smart,
When you're at the dinner table, never let a ...

Swear word pass your lips, please refrain from humming,
Do not tell your best girl so even when you're ...

Coming to the station yard to see the engines shunt,
A piece of steel flew off the wheel and hit her in the ...

Country Girls are pretty lying in the grass,
They kick their legs up over and show their dirty ...

Ask old Brown to supper, ask old Brown to tea,
If he doesn't come, just tickle his bum with a stick of celery.

Cock a doodle doo, cock a doodle doo,
If he doesn't come, just tickle his bum with a cock a doodle doo.

Boy Meets Girl

Boy meets girl, holds her hand,
Visions of a promised land,
Tender words, cling and kiss,
Crafty feel, heavenly bliss,
Nibble nipples, squeeze thighs,
Gets a beat, feels a rise,
Eyes ablaze, drawers down,
Really starts to go to town,
Legs outspread, virgin lass,
Fanny foams like bottled Bass,
Ram it home, moans of joy,
Teenage love, girl meets boy,
Love's a jewel, pearls he's won,
Shoots his load, what's he done?
Comes the pay off, here's the rub,
He's got her in the pudding club,
Comes the wedding, bridesmaids flap,
Love and cherish, all that crap,
A tubby tum, weighty gain,
Prams and nappies, labour pain,
Begins to realise what he did,
Nagging wife and screaming kid,
Sweats his balls off, works his stint:
All the same, he's always skint,
Only pleasure is evening when
Mattress creaks, she's off again,
Can't forsake those sexy habits,
Breeding kids like bloody rabbits.

The Gay Caballero

(Gay in its proper sense; happy, mirthful).

There once was a gay Caballero,
An exceedingly gay Caballero,
A'flashing the end of Maralta Mari,
Maralta, Maralta Mari.

He went to a low down casino,
An exceedingly low down casino,
And of course he took with him etc etc.

He there met a fair Senorita,
An exceedingly fair Senorita,
And of course he suggested etc etc.

He lay her down on a sofita,
An exceedingly fair sofita,
And he gave her nine inches etc etc.

He caught a bad dose of clapita,
An exceedingly bad dose of clapita,
Right on the end of etc etc.

He went to a learned Physiciano,
An exceedingly learned Physiciano,
Who cut off the end etc etc.

And now that my story is ended,
All those whom my song has offended,
Can suck what is left etc etc.

The Gay Caballeroo #2

There was once a Gay Caballero
Who lived in Rio de Janeiro
And called his John Thomas...

CHORUS: *Miralto Maree,*
                Miralto, Miralto, Miralto Maree.

He went to a low-down thee-atre
An exceedingly low-down thee-atre
And of course took with him...

He saw there a fair Senhorita
And he made an appointment to meet her
To introduce her to...

He showed her bull fights in the Corso
And she gazed at the Picador's torso
Which lowered the lance of...

He took her to dine at a Carsa
And filled her with Vino-de-Gaza
And then he suggested...

He took her upstairs to a room-a
And ripped off her crepe-de-chine bloomer
And he showed her his old friend...

She lay on a comfy four-poster
And the cavalier bounded across her
And then he inserted...

But she was a whore from the street-a
And she gave him a roaring clapita
Which blackened the end of...

Next week he had an inspection
An exceedingly thorough inspection
There were spots on the end of...

So he went to a Physiciana
Who lopped off his massive banana
And said, "You must part with..."

So now he's got a strumpeta
And he finds it damn hard to pumpita
He can hardly get hold of...

And the girls in Rio de Janeiro
They give him a jolly good jeer-o
For what he can do with...

And the moral of this small sonita
Is don't fuck a girl when you meet her
But cover the end of Miralto Maree
Your old pal Miralto, Miralto Maree.

And now that my story is ended
I hope you will not be offended
If you are, you can fuck what is left of Maree
Miralto, Miralto, Miralto Maree.

Nemesis

My days of youth are over
My torch of life burned out,
What used to be my sex appeal,
Is now my water spout.

Time was when of its own accord,
'Twould from my trousers spring,
But now I've got a full time job
To find the blasted thing.

It used to be amazing,
The way it would behave,
As early every morning,
It stood and watched me shave.

But as old age approaches,
It fair gives me the blues
To see it hang its withered head
And watch me clean my shoes.

A Street in Cairo

(Tune – Abide with me)

There's a street in Cairo,
Full of sin and shame,
Share el Berka is its fucking name.

CHORUS   *Russian, French and Greek bints*
            All around I see,
            Come all you Air Force lads,
            Abide with me.

When it comes to Friday
And the Airman gets his pay,
Down to *Share el Berka*
I wend my weary way.

Three or four days later
I inspect my 'Hampton Wick'
Go and gets my small kit.
Join the special sick.

Syph and sores and chancres
All around I see,
Crying out "You Air Force boys,
Abide with me."

Three or four months later,
Free from sin and shame,
Back to that street in Cairo
I wend my way again.

Mad Carew

(Monologue)

There's a One-eyed Yellow Idol to the North of Khatmandu,
There's a little broken cross beneath the town,
There's a broken-hearted woman tends the grave of Mad Carew,
While the Yellow God forever gazes down.

He was known as Mad Carew by the subs of Khatmandu,
He was hotter than I care to tell,
But for all his foolish pranks, he was worshipped by the ranks,
And the Colonel's daughter smiled on him as well.

He had loved her all along with the passion of the strong,
And that she loved him was plain to all,
She was nearly twenty-one and preparations had begun,
To celebrate her birthday with a ball.

She met Mad Carew that day as he dismissed his squad,
And he asked what present she would like from Mad Carew,
And jokingly she told him that nothing else would do,
But the Green Eye of the Little Yellow God.

On the night before the dance Mad Carew seemed in a trance,
And they chaffed him as they puffed at their cigars,
But for once in a while, Mad Carew failed to smile,
And went out into the night beneath the stars.

He arrived back next morn with his shirt and tunic torn,
An ugly gash across his forehead dripping red,
Hastily they bathed him and placed him on his bed,
And the Colonel's daughter watched him through the night.

He awoke at last and bade her fetch his tunic in,
And thanked her with a nod and told her to search his pockets,
Saying, "That's from Mad Carew",
It was the Green Eye of the Little Yellow God.

She upbraided Mad Carew in the way that women do,
Though her eyes were soft and strangely wet,
She left him for a while and Mad Carew was left alone,
With the jewel he'd risked his life to get.

On that still and tragic night, when the ball was at its height,
She thought of him and hastened to his room,
As she crossed the barrack square, she could hear faintly the air,
Of a dreamy waltz-tune drifting through the gloom.

The door was open wide and the room shone bright inside,
The floor was wet and sticky where she trod,
And an ugly knife lay buried in the heart of Mad Carew,
'Twas the vengeance of the Little Yellow God.

There's a One-eyed Yellow Idol to the North of Khatmandu,
There's a little broken cross beneath the town,
There's a broken-hearted woman tends the grave of Mad Carew.
While the Yellow God forever gazes down.

Butchers

(Recitation)

The butchers had choppers: *put it on the block, chop it off.*
The barmaids had candles: *pull it out, pull it out, pull it out.*
The cyclists had pedals: *round and round, round and round.*
The flutists had flutes: *root diddly-oot-diddly-oot.*
The painters had brushes: *wop it up and down, up and down.*
The horsemen had saddles: *ride it up and down, up and down.*
The carpenters had hammers: *bang away, bang away, bang away.*
The surgeons had knives: *cut it round the knob, make it throb.*
The parsons had very great alarm: *goodness gracious me!*
The fishermen had rods: *mine is six feet long.*
The huntsmen had horns: *wake up in the morn with a horn.*
The coalmen had sacks: *want it in the front or back?*

The Joys of Copulation

(Tune – John Peel)

CHORUS   *Cats on the rooftops, Cats on the tiles,*
Cats with Syphilis, Cats with piles,
Cats with their arseholes wreathed in smiles,
As they revel in the joys of fornication [copulation].

The Regimental Sergeant Major leads a miserable life,
He can't afford a mistress and he doesn't have a wife,
So he puts it up the bottom of the Regimental Fife,
As he revels in the joys of copulation.

When you find yourself in Springtime with a surge of sexual joy,
And your wife has got the rags on and your daughter's rather coy,
Then jam it up the jacksie of your favourite choirboy,
As you revel in a smooth ejaculation.

Long-legged Curates grind like goats,
Pale-faced spinsters shag like stoats,
And the whole damned world stands by and gloats
As they revel in the joys of copulation.

The ape is small and rather slow,
Erect he stands a foot or so,
So when he comes, it's time to go,
When he revels in the joys of fornication.

Now the hairy old gorilla is a sedentary ape,
Who very seldom does much rape,
But when he does, he comes like tape,
As he revels in the joys of copulation.

The orang-utan is a colourful sight,
There's a glow on his arse like a pilot light,
As it jumps and it leaps in the dead of night
And revels in the joys of copulation.

The flea disports among the trees,
And there consorts with whom he please,
To fill the land with bastard fleas
As he revels in the joys of copulation.

The ostrich is the desert chick,
Without the opportunity to dip his wick,
But when he does, he slips in quick,
As he revels in the joys of fornication.

The donkey [African mule] is a lonely bloke [solitary moke],
He hardly ever gets a poke,
But when he does, he lets it soak,
As he revels in the joys of fornication.

The Hippopotamus [Brontosaurus] so it seems,
Very seldom has wet dreams,
But when he does, he comes in streams,
As he revels in the joys of fornication.

The poor rhinoceros, so it appears,
Never gets a grind in a thousand years,
But when he does, he makes up for arrears
As he revels in the joys of copulation.

The elephant's cock is big and round,
A small one scales a thousand pound,
Two together rock on the ground
As they revel in the joys of copulation.

The camel likes to have his fun,
His night is made when he is done,
He always gets two humps for one,
As he revels in the joys of copulation.

The poor old desert camel has no water for a week,
And as he doesn't drink, the poor bugger cannot leak,
So he has to hold his water, so to speak,
As he revels in the joys of copulation.

Poor old bovine, poor old bull,
Very seldom gets a pull,
But when he does, the cow is full,
As he revels in the joys of copulation.

The Australian lady emu, when she wants to find a mate,
Wanders round the desert with a feather up her date,
You should see that feather when she meets her destined fate,
As she revels in the joys of copulation.

The poor domestic doggie on the chain all day,
Never gets a chance to let himself go gay,
So he licks at his dick in a frantic way
As he revels in the joys of copulation.

The labours of the poofters find little favour here,
But the morally leprous bastard has a peaceful sleep, I fear,
As he dreams he rips a red'un up some dirty urchin's rear,
As he revels in the joys of copulation.

The poor old Creeping Jesus, of his morals there's no doubt,
He walks around St Kilda with his doodle hanging out,
And when he sees a wench it up and hits him in the snout,
As he revels in the joys of copulation.

The dainty little skylark sings a very pretty song,
He has a pond'rous penis fully forty cubits long,
You should hear his high crescendo when his mate is on the prong,
As he revels in the joys of copulation.

The owls in the trees and the cats on the tiles,
One fucks in solitude, the other fucks in files,
You can hear delighted howls and shrieks for miles
As they revel in the joys of copulation.

The whale is a mammal as everybody knows,
He takes two days to have a shag, but when he's in the throes,
He doesn't stop to take it out, he piddles thro' his nose
As he revels in the joys of copulation.

The lady by the seaside was feeling very blue.
She saw the children at it and she thought it wouldn't do,
So she bought three bananas and she ate the other two,
As she revelled in the joys of copulation.

Little Mary Johnson will be seven next July.
She's never had a naughty but she thought she'd like to try,
So she took her Daddy's walking stick and did it on the sly,
As she revelled in the joys of copulation.

In Egypt's sunny clime the crocodile
Gets a flip only once in a while,
But when he does, it floods the Nile,
As he revels in the joys of copulation.

The old wild boar in the mud all day,
Thinks of the sows that are far, far away,
And the corkscrew motion of half a day
As it revels in the joys of copulation.

Poor little tortoise in his shell,
Doesn't manage very well,
But when he does, he fucks like Hell,
As he revels in the joys of copulation.

The oyster is a paragon of purity,
And you cannot tell the he from the she,
But he can tell and so can she,
As they revel in the joys of copulation.

Bow-legged women shit like goats,
Bald-headed men all fuck like stoats,
While the congregation sits and gloats,
And revels in the joys of copulation.

Now I met a girl and she was a dear,
But she gave me a dose of Gonorrhoea,
Fools rush in where Angels fear
To revel in the joys of copulation.

The dirty little bed-bug has his morale torn to bits,
When he sees a husband playing with his wife's rosy tits,
So he searches out and fornicates a thousand million nits
And he revels in the joys of copulation.

When you wake up in the morning and you're feeling full of joy,
And your wife isn't willing and your daughter isn't coy,
Then you've got to use the arsehole of your eldest boy,
As you revel in the joys of copulation.

When you wake up in the morning with a ten inch stand,
From the pressure of the liquid on the seminary gland,
Then there's nothing for it but to use either hand,
As you revel in the joys of masturbation.

When you wake up in the morning and your pecker's on a stand,
From the pressure of your bladder on the prostate gland,
Just let it come with either hand,
As you revel in the joys of masturbation.

When you wake up in the morning with the devil of a stand,
From the pressure of the liquid on the seminary gland,
If you haven't got a woman use your own horny hand
As you revel in the joys of masturbation.

A thousand verses all in rhyme,
To sit and sing them seems a crime,
When we could better spend our time
And revel in the joys of copulation.

Virgin Sturgeon

Caviar comes from the virgin sturgeon.
The male sturgeon's a very fine fish.
The virgin sturgeon needs no urgin'.
That's why caviar is my dish.

I fed caviar to my girlfriend.
She was a virgin tried and true.
Ever since she had that caviar,
There is nothing she won't do.

I took my girlfriend to a surgeon,
Just to see what he could do.
Said that surgeon, "She's no virgin,
Where's the cash? Or no can do."

Shad roe comes from a harlot shadfish.
Shad fish have a sorry fate.
A pregnant shadfish is a sad fish,
Gets that way without a mate.

Oyster are prolific bivalves,
They have young ones in their shell,
How they piddle is a riddle,
But they do – sure as hell!

The green sea-turtle's mate is happy
O'er her lover's winning ways:
First he grips her with a flipper,
Then he flips for days and days.

The lady clam is optimistic,
Shoots her eggs out in the sea,
She hopes her suitor, as a shooter,
Hits the self-same spot as she.

Give a thought to the canny codfish,
Ever there when duty calls,
The female codfish is an oddfish,
From her, too, come codfish balls.

The trout is but a little salmon,
Just half-grown and minus scales,
Yet the trout, just like a salmon,
Can't get on without his tail.

Lucky creatures are the rayfish,
When a litter they assay.
Yes, my hearties, they have parties,
In the good old-fashioned way.

I gave caviar to my Grandpa.
Grandpa's age was ninety-three.
Shouts and screams were heard from Grandma.
He had chased her up a tree.

Fed some caviar to my Grandma,
She came right down from that tree,
Now my Grandma and my Grandpa
Start to raise a family.

My Father was a lighthouse keeper.
He had caviar for his tea.
He had three children by a Mermaid.
Two were kippers, one was me.

My Father was the keeper of the Eddystone Light,
He slept with a Mermaid one dark night.
Result of this was off-spring three,
Two were fish and the other was me.

The Chandler's Shop

(Tune – Lincolnshire Poacher)

A lad went into a Chandler's shop, some matches for to buy,
And though he shouted loud and long, no person heard his cry,
And as he paused to gain his breath, he thought he heard a tread,
Oh! He heard the sound of a fuck, right above his head.
Oh! He heard the sound of a fuck, right above his head.

Now being a very curious lad, up the stairs he sped,
And most surprised he was to find the Chandler's wife in bed,
And lying there beside her was a man of considerable size,
Oh! And they were having a fuck, right before his eyes!
Oh! And they were having a fuck, right before his eyes!

Now a warning to you married men, if 'ere you go to town,
If you should have a pretty wife, be sure to tie her down,
Remember well the saying, "Out of sight is out of mind,"
And she may be having a fuck whenever she's inclined.
And she may be having a fuck whenever she's inclined.

Another version...

The boy went into a Chandler's shop,
Some matches for to buy,
He looked around and around he looked,
But no one did he spy.
He cried aloud, aloud he cried,
With a voice to wake the dead,
When he heard a kind of a "Rat-tat-tat", right above his head,
When he heard a kind of a "Rat-tat-tat", right above his head.

Now the boy was of an enquiring mind,
So he quickly climbed the stair,
And the door of the room was open
And the Chandler's wife was there.
The Chandler's wife lay on the bed
A man between her thighs
And they were having a "Rat-tat-tat," right before his eyes,
And they were having a "Rat-tat-tat," right before his eyes.

Oh Boy, oh Boy, my secret keep
And for me tell a lie,
For if the Chandler should hear of this,
He'd beat me till I cry.
And if you promise to be good
I'll always to you be kind,
And you shall have a "Rat-tat-tat," whenever you feel inclined,
And you shall have a "Rat-tat-tat," whenever you feel inclined.

The Chandler returned and entered the shop.
He quickly smelled a rat,
Seeing his wife all naked there
Her hand upon her twat.
The Chandler's wife ran to the room
Expecting the boy had fled,
But he was having a "Rat-tat-tat," all by himself in bed,
But he was having a "Rat-tat-tat," all by himself in bed.

Brown Eyes

(Frank Mortimer, 70 Sqdn Party Piece)

Beautiful, Beautiful, Beautiful Brown Eyes,
Beautiful, Beautiful, Beautiful Brown Eyes,
Beautiful, Beautiful, Beautiful Brown Eyes,
I'll never love Blue Eyes again.

Oh, oh, oh, Vera my darling I love you,
I love you with all my heart,
To think that we could have been married,
Instead of our living apart.

Oh, oh, oh, Beautiful, Beautiful Brown Eyes, [three times]
I'll never love Blue Eyes again.

Oh, oh, oh, out of the ivy she staggered,
He fell down by her side,
The very last words that he uttered,
"Don't these bloody tits hurt when you fall on'em?"

I'll never love Blue Eyes again,
Oh, oh, oh, Beautiful, Beautiful Brown Eyes, [three times]
I'll never love Blue Eyes again.

Chicago

A lady came into the bookshop,
I asked, "What would you like?"
"Felt," she said. Felt'er I did.
I'll never work there any more.

CHORUS: *I used to work in Chicago*
In a department store
I used to work in Chicago
But I don't work there any more.

A lady came in for a waterbottle,
I asked, "What would you like?"
"Rubber," she said. Rub'er I did.
I'll never work there any more.

A lady came in for a sweater,
I asked, "What would you like?"
"Jumper," she said. Jump'er I did.
I'll never work there any more.

A lady came in for a cake,
I asked, "What would you like?"
"Layer," she said. Lay'er I did.
I'll never work there any more.

A lady came in for a ticket,
I asked, "What would you like?"
"Bangor," she said. Bang'er I did.
I'll never work there any more.

A lady came in for a sleeper,
I asked, "What would you like?"
"Upper," she said. Up'er I did.
I'll never work there any more.

My Darling Clementine

(Tune – Clementine)

In a cavern, in a canyon,
Excavating for a mine,
Dwelt a miner, forty-niner
And his daughter Clementine.

CHORUS   *Oh, my darling, oh, my darling,*
                Oh my darling Clementine,
                You are lost and gone for ever,
                Dreadful sorry, Clementine.

Light she was and like a Fairy
And her shoes were number nine,
Herring boxes without topses,
Sandals were for Clementine.

Drove her ducklings to the water,
Every morning just at nine,
Stubbed her toe upon a splinter,
Fell into the foaming brine.

Ruby lips upon the water,
And her hair so soft and fine,
But alas, I was no swimmer,
So I lost my Clementine.

How I missed her, how I missed her,
How I missed my Clementine,
'Till I kissed her little sister,
Better, far, than Clementine!

I Owe me Darlin'

(Another skit on Clementine)

There she stood beside the bar rail
Drinking pink gins for two bits.
And the swollen whiskey barrels
Stood in awe beside her tits.

CHORUS   *I owe my darlin', I owe my darlin',*
                I owe my darlin' Clementine,
                Three bent pennies and a nickel,
                Oh my darlin' Clementine.

Eyes of whiskey, lips of water,
As she sodden at me peer,
Dawns the daylight in her temple,
With a fucking-warming leer.

Hung me guitar on the brass rail,
At the sweetness of the sign,
In one leap leapt out me trousers,
Plunged into the foaming brine.

She was bawdy, she was busty,
She could match the great Buzoom,
As she strained out of her bloomers,
Like a melon tree in bloom.

Oh! The oak tree and the cypress,
Never more together twine,
Since that creeping poison ivy
Laid its blight on Clementine.

Cocaine Bill

Cocaine Bill and Morphine Sue,
Were walking down Fifth Avenue.

CHORUS   *Honey have a (sniff) have a (sniff) on me*
                Honey have a (sniff) on me.

Said Cocaine Bill to his Morphine Moll,
"There ain't no sense in alcohol."

From Broadway to the State of Maine
They went in search of more cocaine.

They came to a drug store painted green,
The sign outside said, "No Morphine."

Into the store went Morphine Sue
To see if the sign meant cocaine too,

They came to a drug store painted red,
The sign it said, "Try Coke instead."

They went down to the riverside
And there committed suicide.

Now in the graveyard on the hill
Lies the body of Cocaine Bill.

From ashes to ashes and dust to dust,
If the Lord don't get you, the cocaine must.

Now this story goes to show
There is no sense in sniffing snow.

Praise my Soul it is the Lord
Coming in to land at Ford,
Listening out on Channel, "B",
Singing, "Honey have a (sniff) have a (sniff) on me."

My Grandfather's Cock

(Tune – Grandfather's Clock)

My Grandfather's cock was too long for his jock,
So it dragged ninety yards on the floor.
It was bigger by far than the old man himself,
And it weighed not a pennyweight more.

With a horn on the morn of the day that he was born,
And a horn on the day that he died,
My Grandfather's cock was too long for his jock,
So it stood for his honour and pride.

Another version (from Oz)

My Grandfather's cock was too long for his pants,
And it dragged several feet on the floor.
It was longer by half than the old man himself,
And it weighed nigh a hundredweight more.

He'd a horn on the morn of the day that he was born,
It was always his pleasure and pride,
But it drooped, shrank, never to rise again,
When the old man died.

CHORUS Ninety years without cracking it (What a cock! What a cock!)

> *He spent his life whacking it, (What a cock! What a cock!)*
> *But it drooped, shrank, never to rise again,*
> *When the old man died.*

My grandfather's cock was too big for his wife,
So he took it to the lady next door.
She grabbed it by the point and pulled it out of joint,
So he swore he'd never lend it any more.

He'd a horn on the morn of the day that he was born,
It was always his pleasure and pride,
But it drooped, shrank, never to rise again,
When the old man died.

Craven A

Listen to my story kindly if you will,
About a bastard born in Muswell Hill.
Born in Muswell Hill but spawned in Camberwell,
And the first words he spoke were, "Bloody Fucking 'ell".

Craven A never heard of copulation
Craven A never dipped his tool
Craven A was quite content with masturbation
Thought a cunt was something you were called at school.

Now Jenny was a prostitute of Cambridge Town.
She gamarouched a Proctor in his cap and gown,
And then she told that Proctor which she didn't ought,
That she'd never seen a bastard with a tool so short.

Now the Proctor very quickly up and told that whore,
He'd a cousin who had never seen a cunt before
And he wrote to Craven A saying quickly pack your things,
For the shooting season opens on the fourth at Kings.

Craven's entry to the Varsity was quite grotesque,
He went and laid his prick upon his Tutor's desk
His Tutor said, "Please bring it at a later date,
I'll be very glad to use it as a paper weight."

The Proctor said to Craven, "One thing I must impress,
Never masturbate in Academic dress,"
But Craven just to show he didn't give a fuck,
Tossed himself off in the teapot shouting, "That's for luck!"

Now quickly Craven found that after they had dined,
All the Undergrads lined up for what they call a grind,
So he hid beneath the bed, despite the awful smell,
And when the others came, Craven came as well.

Now Jenny had a daughter who was small and wee.
She used to take her cunt up with the morning tea.
Now he's up so often that now the Courts declare,
Her vagina constitutes a Legal throroughfare.

The Crayfish

I once met a fisherman, a'fishing by the sea,
I said, "Have you got a Crayfish you could give to me?"

CHORUS   *With a hey-hi-hey-hi-hey-hi-ho,*
                     With a hey-hi-hey-hi-ho.
OR

                     Ro-tiddly-oh, shit or bust,
                     Never let your bollocks dangle in the dust.

"Oh yes," said the fisherman a'fishing by the sea,
"I've got a Crayfish that I'll give to thee."

So I took the Crayfish home just to give my wife a treat,
And I put it in the pisspot to keep the bugger sweet.

Now my wife came home from being out to tea,
She sat upon the pisspot to have a little wee.

Now she pissed upon its back and she pissed upon its side,
She pissed upon the little thing, until it nearly died.

She made the Crayfish wriggle and she made the bugger squirm,
Till it bit her in the place, where she used to get the worm.

Now the moral of my story is very plain to see,
You should look inside the pisspot before you have a wee.

[Now the moral of my story it is this,
Always have a shufti before you have a piss.]

And now my story's over, there isn't any more,
There's an apple up my arse and you can have the core.

Darkie Sunday School

Young folk, old folk, everybody come
To the darkie Sunday School and we'll have lots of fun.
Bring your sticks of chewing gum and sit upon the floor,
And we'll tell you Bible stories that you never heard before.

Now Adam was the first man, so we're led to believe,
He walked into the garden and bumped right into Eve.
There was no one there to show him, but he quickly found the way
And that's the very reason why we're singing here today.

The Lord said unto Noah, "It's going to rain today,"
So Noah built a bloody great ark in which to sail away.
The animals went in two by two, but soon got up to tricks,
So although they came in two by two, they came out six by six.

Now Moses in the bullrushes was all wrapped up the swathe,
Pharaoh's daughter found him when she went down there to bathe.
She took him back to Pharaoh and said, "I found him on the shore,"
And Pharaoh winked his eye and said, "I've heard that one before."

King Solomon and King David lived most immoral lives,
Spent their time a'chasing other people's wives.
The Lord spake unto both of them and it worked just like a charm,
'Cos Solomon wrote the Proverbs and David wrote the Psalms.

Now Samson was an Israelite and very big and strong,
Delilah was a Philistine, always doing wrong.
They spent a week together but it didn't get very hot,
For all he got was a short back and sides and a little off the top.

The Boy Stood on the Burning Deck

The boy stood on the burning deck,
His arse against the mast.
He said he would not move a step
Till Oscar Wilde had passed.

CHORUS   *Star of the evening,*
                 pretty little evening staaaar,
                 Star of the evening,
                 shining on the shithouse door.

But Oscar was a wily bird,
He threw the boy a plum,
And when he bent to pick it up,
He leaped upon his bum.

But the boy was up to all the tricks,
He'd been to Public School.
He gave his pretty arse a twist
And fractured Oscar's tool.

A whore from Baroda

There was a young whore from Baroda,
Who kept an unusual pagoda.
The walls of her halls were hung with the balls
And the tools of the fools who bestrode her.

Chin Chin Chinaman

Chin Chin Chinaman, walking down the Strand,
Stony-broke, wants a poke, penis in his hand,
Up comes Posy Lil, he doesn't give a rap,
Three days later, CLAP, CLAP, CLAP!

The Old Farmer

There was an old farmer who stood on a rick,
Shouting and swearing and waving his...

Fist at the Sailors who sat on the rocks,
Teaching the children to play with their...

Kites and their marbles as in days of yore,
When along came a lady who looked like a...

Decent young lady, she walked like a duck,
She said she was teaching a new way to...

Educate the children, to sew and to knit,
While the boys in the stables were shovelling the...

Contents of the stables, the muck and the mud,
The dirty old Squire was pulling his...

Horse from the stable to go on a hunt,
His wife in her boudoire was powdering her...

Nose and arranging her vanity box,
And taking precautions to ward off the...

Gout and rheumatics, which left her so stiff,
How well she remembered her last dose of...

What do you think I was going to say?
You dirty old bastards, that's all for today.

Definitions

Adultery	Two wrong people doing the right thing.
Alimony	The screwing you get after the screwing you got.
Ballrace	A Tom cat with a twenty yard start on the vet.
Baltic	A venereal parasite.
Blackout	The reason why a girl is apt to get blown into maternity without knowing who is responsible.
Blunderbuss	A bus full of bastards.
Brassiere	A device for making mountains out of molehills.
Chivalry	A man's inclination to protect a woman from every man but himself.
Clerical Error	A Nun finding the seat up.
Divorce	What happens to people who cannot stomach each other any longer.
Endless Belt	A Sailor's leave.
Glamour Girl	A much publicised young lady who is occasionally full of oomph and frequently full of other things.
Green Belt	A girl's first night out with a sailor.
Hysterectomy	Removing the nursery but leaving the playpen.
Interlude	The time between times.
Kiss	Uptown shopping in downtown business.
Metallurgist	A man who can take a look at a platinum blonde and tell if it's virgin metal or just common ore.
Mistress	Something between a mister and a mattress.
Mother's Day	Nine months after Father's Day.
Nurse	A pan handler.
Nursery	The place to store last years' fun until it grows up.
Old Maid	A girl of advanced years who has gone through life with no hits, no misses and no errors.
Outdoor Girl	One with the bloom of youth in her cheeks and the cheek of youth in her bloomers.
Pansy	One who likes his vice versa.

Papoose	Consolation prize for taking a chance on an Indian blanket.
Passion	A feeling you get when you feel you are feeling a feeling you haven't felt before.
Pregnancy	A woman swelled up over her man's handiwork.
Private Secretary	A girl who never misses a period.
Prostitute	A busybody.
Psychiatrist	A man who tries to figure out whether infants in infancy have more fun than adults in adultery.
Puff Adders	A person who blows off in the bath and counts the bubbles.
Pyjamas	Clothes newly-weds place by the side of the bed in case of fire.
Rape	Seduction without salesmanship.
Spouse	A combined domestic servant, hot water bottle and incubator.
Sob Sister	A girl who sits on your knee and makes it hard for you.
Spring	When a young man's fancy turns to what a woman has been thinking of all Winter.
Spring Fever	When the iron in your blood turns to lead in your pencil.
Step-ins	A lady's last line of defence. They go on easily but have to be coaxed off.
Stockings	Feminine coverings which either come up to a lady's expectations or tickle her fancy.
Stork	The bird that has all the work and none of the fun.
Strapadictomy	Medical term for lesbianism.
Taxidermist	A man who mounts animals.
Triplets	Taking seriously what was only poked at you in fun.
Twins	Womb mates, who eventually become bosom pals.
Virgin Sheep	One who can run faster than the shepherd.
Weakling	A girl who means "No" but can't say it.

• •

Dinah, Dinah, Show Us Your Leg

A rich girl has a limousine,
A poor girl has a truck,
But the only time that Dinah rides
Is when she has a fuck.

Dinah, Dinah, show us your leg,
Show us your leg, show us your leg.
Dinah, Dinah, show us your leg
A yard above your knee.

A rich girl has a brassiere,
A poor girl uses string,
But Dinah uses nothing at all,
She lets the bastards swing.

A rich girl has a ring of gold,
A poor girl has one of brass,
But the only ring that Dinah has
Is the one around her arse.

A rich girl uses Vaseline,
A poor girl uses lard,
But Dinah uses axle-grease
Because her cunt's so hard.

A rich girl uses a sanitary towel,
A poor girl uses a sheet,
But Dinah uses nothing at all,
Leaves a trail along the street.

The Dirge Of 849

(Tune – Eton Boating Song)

They're lowering the standards for Aircrew,
General List Officers as well,
Observers get lost in the BUNDU,
And Pilots get drunk in the BELL.

CHORUS   *Oh! We'll all pull together,*
              The A48 as well,
              Oh! We'll all pull together,
              For flying the Gannet is Hell.

They're lowering the standards for Aircrew,
Pilots who can't read or write,
By day they just sleep or drink coffee,
And go GAFFING women at night.

They're lowering the standards for Aircrew,
Men you won't normally meet,
They get drunk on Brandy and Whisky,
And they park COOKIES right in the street.

They're lowering the standards for Aircrew,
Don't know how an aeroplane works,
It's all this new co-education,
At school they just learn to lift skirts.

They're lowering the standards for Aircrew,
Some Pilots act quite strange and coy,
This often confuses the MO,
Who can't decide if SHE'S a BOY.

They're lowering the standards for Aircrew,
It's all dirty books, film shows too,
They ask fifteen shillings to see them.
We all pay our cash – wouldn't you?

They're lowering the standards for Aircrew,
Lowsee and mutuals by night,
By day we do Distrike and Recce,
All work and no play – is it right?

They're lowering the standards for Aircrew,
It's all sex and drinking and mirth,
Ask the Boss what he'd do as a CO,
He'll say, "Have them strangled at birth".

Now all you young maidens forgive us,
If we seduce you – or worse,
Don't blame the poor men, blame the system,
For standards go on getting worse.

Some Die Of Drinking Water

(Tune – British Grenadiers)

Some die of drinking water,
Some die of drinking beer,
Some die of constipation,
And some of diarrhoea,
But of all the world's diseases
There's none that can compare
With the drip, drip, drip
Of a syphilitic dick [fanny]
And they call it gonorrhoea.

The Girls I like

I like the girls who say they will.
I like the girls who won't,
I hate the girls who say they will
And then they say they won't,
But of all the girls I like the best,
I may be wrong or right,
Are the girls who say they never will
But look as though they might!

Life Presents a Dismal Picture

(Tune – German National Anthem)

Life presents a dismal picture,
Dark and silent as the tomb,
Father has an anal stricture,
Mother has a fallen womb.

Sister Sue has been aborted,
For the forty-second time,
Brother Bill has been deported
For a homosexual crime.

Nurse has chronic menstruation,
Never laughs and never smiles,
Mine's a dismal [genial] occupation,
Cracking ice for Grandpa's piles.

In a small brown-paper parcel,
Wrapped in a mysterious way,
Is an imitation rectum,
Grandad uses twice a day.

Even now the baby's started
Having epileptic fits,
Every time it coughs it vomits
And every time it farts it shits.

Little Johnny, masturbating,
Pulled his penis much too hard
And the heat he generated,
Turned his bollocks into lard.

Yet we are not broken-hearted,
Neither are we up the spout,
Auntie Mabel [Uncle Jimmy] has just farted,
Blown her arsehole [his rectum] inside out.

The Farmer's Dog

A farmer's dog once came to town,
Whose Christian name was Pete.
His pedigree was ten yards long,
His looks were hard to beat.

As he trotted down the road,
It was beautiful to see,
His work on every corner,
His mark on every tree.

He watered every gateway,
He never missed a post,
For piddling was his masterpiece
And piddling was his boast.

The city dogs stood looking on
With deep and jealous rage,
To see this simple country dog,
The piddler of the age.

They smelt him over one by one,
They smelt him two by two,
The noble Pete in high disdain,
Stood still till they were through.

And as they sniffed him over,
Their praise for him ran high,
But one sniffed him underneath,
Pete piddled in his eye.

Then just to show those city dogs
He didn't give a damn,
Pete strolled into a grocer's shop,
And piddled on some ham.

He piddled on the onions,
He piddled on the floor,
And when the grocer kicked him out,
Pete piddled on the door.

Behind him all the city dogs
Debated what to do,
They'd hold a piddling carnival
And show him who was who!

They showed Pete all the piddling posts,
They knew about the town.
They started out with merry winks
To get this stranger down.

But Pete was with them every trick,
With vigour and with vim,
A thousand piddles more or less,
Were all the same to him.

And on and on went noble Pete
With hind leg kicking high,
While most were lifting legs in bluff,
Or piddling mighty dry.

And on and on went noble Pete
And watered every sandhill,
Till all the city champions
Were piddled to a standstill.

Then Pete an exhibition gave
In all the ways to piddle,
Like double drips and fancy flips
And now and then a dribble.

While all the time the country dog
Did neither wink nor grin,
But piddled blithely out of town,
As he had piddled in.

The city dogs said, "So, long Pete,
Your piddling did defeat us!"
But no one ever put them wise,
That Pete had diabetes.

The Doggies' Meeting

The doggies held a meeting
They came from near and far,
Some came by motor-cycle,
Some by motor-car.
Each doggy passed the entrance,
Each doggy signed the book,
Then each unshipped his arsehole
And hung it on a hook.

One dog was not invited,
It sorely raised his ire.
He ran into the meeting hall
And loudly bellowed, "FIRE!"
It threw them in confusion
And without a second look
Each grabbed another's arsehole
From off another hook.

And that's the reason why, Sir,
When walking down the street,
And that's the reason why, Sir,
When doggies chance to meet,
And that's the reason why, Sir,
On land or sea or foam,
He will sniff another's arsehole
To see if it's his own.

Deadeye Dick (Again)

This is the tale of Deadeye Dick.
He was the man with the corkscrew prick.
He searched the world on a fruitless hunt
To find a girl with a corkscrew cunt
And when he found her, he dropped down dead,
Because she had a left-hand thread.

The Old Red Flannel Drawers that Maggie Wore

When she got them they were fluffy,
Now they're faded and they're scruffy,
The old Red Flannel Drawers that Maggie wore.

They were hemmed in, they were tucked in,
They were the drawers that she was married in,
Those old Red Flannel Drawers that Maggie wore.

They were rotten down the front
With the dripping of her cunt,
Those old Red Flannel Drawers that Maggie wore.

When she sent them to the laundry,
They were seen by all and sundry,
The old Red Flannel Drawers that Maggie wore.

She put them in the sink,
My God! There was a stink
From the Old Red Flannel Drawers that Maggie wore.

The Aircrew laughed and grinned,
When they came up to her chin,
The old Red Flannel Drawers that Maggie wore.

She daren't try to sneeze,
They would fall down to her knees,
The old Red Flannel Drawers that Maggie wore.

She said, "Pack up, that's enough,"
When we tried to take them off,
The old Red Flannel Drawers that Maggie wore.

She was sometimes sick with fright,
'Cos the elastic was too tight,
In the old Red Flannel Drawers that Maggie wore.

She'd run through the pickers,
When they said, "Show us your knickers,"
The old Red Flannel Drawers that Maggie wore.

They were padded with a bit of rag,
Where someone had dropped a fag,
On the old Red Flannel Drawers that Maggie wore.

She put them on the mat
And paralysed the cat,
Those old red flannel drawers that Maggie wore.

She went out with a second Dickie,
But he tried to take the Mickey,
Out of the old Red Flannel Drawers that Maggie wore.

There was the band of Harry James,
She'd sewed all their names,
On the old Red Flannel Drawers that Maggie wore.

She went out with a Soldier,
They came back a little bit mouldier,
The old Red Flannel Drawers that Maggie wore.

The night she went with Taffy,
They were found behind the NAAFI,
The old Red Flannel Drawers that Maggie wore.

When on the line she hung'em,
You could almost see right through'em,
The old Red Flannel Drawers that Maggie wore.

When she put them on the line,
The sun refused to shine
For the old red flannel drawers that Maggie wore.

One day in her vest she stood,
They were wrapped round the Christmas pud,
The old Red Flannel Drawers that Maggie wore.

She wouldn't go with Groupie,
'Cos she said they were too droopy,
The old Red Flannel Drawers that Maggie wore.

They were tattered, they were torn,
Round the breezehole they were worn,
The old Red Flannel Drawers that Maggie wore.

She buried them in the ground,
Killed the grass for miles around,
Those old red flannel drawers that Maggie wore.

One day for a prank,
Someone tied them to a Lanc,
The old Red Flannel Drawers that Maggie wore.

They all went on an op,
And they all got the chop,
With the old Red Flannel Drawers that Maggie wore.

Sister Lily

Have you met my Uncle Hector?
He's a cock and ball inspector
At a celebrated English Public School,
And my Brother sells French Letters
And a patent cure for wetters.
We're not the best of families – ain't it cruel?

My little Sister Lily is a whore in Piccadilly.
My Mother is another in the Strand.
My Father hawks his arsehole
At the Elephant and Castle.
We're the finest fucking family in the land.

I Dreamed My Love

I dreamed my love lay in her bed,
It was my chance to take her,
Her legs and arms abroad were spread.
She slept, I dared not wake her.

O pity it were that one so fair
Should crown her love with willow.
The tresses of her golden hair
Did kiss her lonely pillow.

Methought her belly was a hill
Much like a mount of pleasure,
Under whose brow there grows a well,
Whose depth no man can measure.

About the pleasant mountain top
There grows a lovely thicket,
Wherein my two hounds travelled
And raised a lively prickett.

They hunted here with pleasant noise
About the ferny mountain,
'Till heat the prickett forced to fly
And skip into the fountain.

The hounds they followed to the brink
And there at him they barked,
He plunged about but would not shrink
His coming forth they waited.

Then forth he came as one half lame,
Limp, weary, faint and tired
And laid him down between her legs,
For help he had required.

The hounds they were refreshed again,
My love from sleep returned
And dreamed she held me in her arms
And she was not alarmed.

A Shilling a Go

(Tune – One Man Went to Mow)

Down in Drury Lane there are some filthy women.
You can get a bit of you know what all for a shilling.
Soldiers half a crown, sailors half a guinea,
Ordinary men two pounds ten, schoolboys all a penny.

Three whores walk the streets, always bloody willing.
It's only a bob for a bit of knob, all for a shilling.

In the Shetland Isles there are no filthy women.
You can take a leap at any old sheep, all for a shilling.
NCOs two, Airmen one and sixpence.
You can have a screw on the old black ewe, all for a shilling.

In the Middle East there's bags of filthy women.
In the crack or up the back, all for a shilling.
Frenchmen pay five francs, Doughboys pay a dollar.
You can shoot your cream in the old harem, all for a shilling.

Out in India there are no filthy memsahibs.
So what do the pukka wallahs get for their shilling?
Knotholes in the floor or the hole in the elephant's bottom,
But in Calcutta you can grind in the gutter, all for a shilling.

On the ocean waves there are no filthy Wrens, Sir,
So what does poor Jack Tar get for a shilling?
Admirals keep a goat, Captains have a parrot,
But the Matelot true has a good blow through, all for a shilling.

The Old Woman Of Dublin

There was an old woman in Dublin did dwell,
And the dirty old bitch I knew her quite well,
She went to the country for a holiday.
She was goosed right and left before she got away.

CHORUS   *Toor-a-loo, toor-a-lay, it's a bloody fine song*
                I could sing it all day:
                Toor-a-loo, not a bit, it's a bloody fine song,
                But it's all about shit.

She got up in the night for she wanted the pot,
Which perchance the old slave entirely forgot,
Said she, "I can't help it if things come to pass,"
So she upped wide the winder and stuck out her arse.

A smart young Policeman was walking his beat,
Which happened to be in that part of the street:
He gazed at the stars as they shone in the sky,
And a bit of soft shit caught him right in the eye.

And this is the trouble that old bitch did cause,
That poor young Policeman was axed from the Force,
And if you go to Dublin you can see him sit,
Wid a card round his neck, saying, "Blinded by shit."

Fanny Bay

(Tune – Galway Bay)

If you ever go across the sea to Darwin,
Then maybe at the closing of the day,
You will see the local harlots at their business
And watch the sun go down on Fanny Bay.

Some are black and some are white and some are brindle,
And some are young and some are old and grey,
But what will cost you twenty quid in Lower Crown Street,
Will cost you half a zac in Fanny Bay.

Nightwatchman

Tune: Villikens

Down in Old London a harlot did dwell
The dirty old bitch, I knew her so well.
On one Summer evening these things came to pass,
She opened the window and shoved out her arse.

Dinkie-die, dinkie-die,
She opened the window and shoved out her arse.

Now a poor old night-watchman was just passing by,
And the poor old night-watchman was eating a pie.
The poor old night-watchman looked up to the sky,
And a steaming hot turd hit him fair in the eye.

Dinkie-die, dinkie-die,
A steaming hot turd hit him fair in the eye.

The poor old night-watchman was blinded for life
With twenty-four kids and a prostitute wife:
Down at the corner you can still see him sit,
"Spare a coin Sir, spare a coin Sir,
For I'm blinded by shit".

Dinkie-die, dinkie-die,
Spare a coin Sir, spare a coin Sir, for I'm blinded by shit.

Bawdy Ballads

The Hole in the Elephant's Bottom

My ambition's to go on the stage
And now my ambition I've gotten,
In Pantomime I'm all the rage,
As the hole in the elephant's bottom.

The Manager says, "It's all balls,"
But somehow I manage to spot 'em
And wink at the whores in the stalls
Through the hole in the elephant's bottom.

The Manager knows I'm a fool,
When the elephant's tail I've forgotten,
But I hang my magnificent tool
Through the hole in the elephant's bottom.

I'm a lover of beautiful girls:
Yes, ladies I've always been hot on,
I turn around and wink at the stuff in the stalls
Through the hole in the elephant's bottom.

My part doesn't have any words,
So it really cannot be forgotten,
I simply drop property turds
Through the hole in the elephant's bottom.

Two Nancy-boys came in one day,
And before anyone could stop 'em,
They handed a lovely bouquet
Through the hole in the elephant's bottom.

The fellow who plays the front part,
As an actor is just bloody rotten,
He simply does nothing but fart,
And *I* am the elephant's bottom.

The Chorus girls wear crepe-de-chine drawers
And the sweat makes the fabric go rotten.
When they burst, there are roars of applause
From the hole in the elephant's bottom.

Two pockets I've cut in the cloth,
For two bottles of beer when I've got 'em,
Folks laugh as I blow out the froth
Through the hole in the elephant's bottom.

There are many more words in this song
But I'm sorry to say I forgot 'em,
If you've found this song just a bit too long,
You can all kiss the elephant's bottom.

Get Hold of This

(Recitation)

Little Miss Muffet sat on a tuffet, eating her curds and whey,
There came a big spider and sat down beside her,
He whipped his old bazooka out and this is what he said:

"Get hold of this (Bang, Bang!) get hold of this (Bang, Bang!)
When there isn't a girl about you feel so lonely:
When there isn't a girl about you're on your owny.
Absolutely on the self, nothing to do but play with yourself,
When there isn't a girl about."

Little Jack Horner sat in a corner,
Lookng at dirty postcards, giving himself a thrill.
He looked all around and saw no one was near so
He whipped his old bazooka out and this is what he said:

"Get hold of this (Bang, Bang!) get hold of this (Bang, Bang!)
When there isn't a girl about you feel so lonely:
When there isn't a girl about you're on your owny.
Absolutely on the self, nothing to do but play with yourself,
When there isn't a girl about."

The Ballad Of Eskimo Nell

[There are all sorts of versions!]

Gather round all you whorey,
Gather round and hear this story.

So gather round you trusty men,
        A tale to you I'll tell
[So pull up a chair and stand me a drink
        and a tale to you I'll tell]
Of a lusty maid who was ne'er afraid,
        whose name was Eskimo Nell.
[Of Dead-eye Dick and Mexican Pete
        and a harlot called Eskimo Nell.]

When a man grows old and his balls grow cold
And the tip of his prick turns blue,
And it bends in the middle like a one string fiddle,
He can tell you a tale or two.

When Dead-eyed Dick and Mexican Pete
Go forth in search of fun,
It's Dead-eyed Dick who swings the prick
And Mexican Pete the gun.
And when Dead-eyed Dick and Mexican Pete
Are feeling depressed and sad,
It's always a cunt that bears the brunt,
Though the shootin' ain't so bad.

Now Dead-eyed Dick and Mexican Pete
Had been working Dead Man's Creek
And they'd had no luck in the way of a fuck
For well-nigh on a week.
Just a moose or two, a caribou
And a bison-cow or so
And for Dead-eyed Dick, the King of pricks,
The fucking was too damned slow.

So Dead-eyed Dick and Mexican Pete
[So do or dare, this horny pair ...]
Set forth for the Rio Grande,
Dead-eyed Dick with a solid prick
And Pete with a gun in his hand.
And as they blazed their noisy trail,
No man their path withstood
And many a bride, who was hubby's pride,
A pregnant widow stood [knew pregant widowhood].

They hit the banks of the Rio Grande
By a Creek called Burning Moon
And to slake their thirst and to do their worst,
They sought Black Mike's saloon.
So crashing through the swinging doors
Both gun and prick flashed free
"According to sex you bleeding wrecks,
You drinks or fucks with me."

They knew the prick of Dead-eye Dick
From Cape Horn to the Panama,
So with nothing worse than a muffled curse,
Those Dagoes sought the bar.
And the women too, knew a trick or two,
Down on the Rio Grande,
So forty whores tore down their drawers
At Dead-eye Dick's command.

They saw the fingers of Mexican Pete
Twitch on his pistol grip,
'Twas death to wait, at a fearful rate
Those whores began to strip
And Dead-eye Dick was breathing quick
With lecherous snorts and grunts,
As forty arses were bared to view,
To say nothing of forty cunts.

Now forty arses and forty cunts
You'll know if you use your wits
And if you're slick at arithmetic,
It'll add up to eighty tits.
Now eighty tits are a gladsome sight
To a man with a raging stand.
It might be rare in Berkeley Square,
But not on the Rio Grande.

Now Dead-eye Dick had fucked a few
On the preceding night:
This he had done just to show his fun
And to whet his appetite.
So his phallic limb was in fucking trim
As he backed and took a run.
He made a dart at the nearest tart
And scored a bull in one.

He bore her to the sandy floor
And fairly fucked her fine
And though she grinned, it put the wind
Up the other thirty-nine.
For when Dead-eye Dick performs his trick,
He's got no time to spare,
For speed and strength combined with length,
He fairly singes hair.

Now Dead-eye Dick he screws them quick,
So he flung the first aside
And made a dart for the second tart,
When the big swing-doors swung wide.
And there entered in to that hall of sin,
Into that harlot's hell,
A lusty maid, who was unafraid,
Whose name was Eskimo Nell.

Now Dead-eye Dick had got his prick
Well into number twenty-two,
When Eskimo Nell let out a yell
And bawled at him, "Hey you!"
So he gave a flick of his muscular prick
And the girl flew over his head
And with a sneering shout he turned about
And his face and tool were red.

But Eskimo Nell she stood it well
And looked him between the eyes.
She scanned his horn with utmost scorn
As it rose from his heaving thighs.
[She glanced our hero up and down,
His looks she seemed to decry,
With utmost scorn she glimpsed the horn
That rose from his hairy thigh]
She puffed a whiff of her cigarette
Right over his steaming knob,
So utterly beat was Mexican Pete
That he forgot to do his job.

'Twas Eskimo Nell who broke the spell
In accents clear and cool,
"You cunt-struck shrimp of a Yankee pimp,
Do you call that thing a tool?
If this little town can't take that down,"
She sneered at the cowering whores,
"There's one little cunt that'll do the stunt,
And it's Eskimo Nell's, not yours."

She stripped her garments one by one
With an air of conscious pride
And there she stood in her womanhood
And they saw the great divide.
She seated herself on a table-top
Where someone had left a glass
With a twitch of tits she crushed it to bits
Between the cheeks of her arse.

With effortless ease she raised her knees
And opened them wide apart
And with a friendly nod to the mangy sod,
She gave him his cue to start.
But Dead-eye Dick knew many a trick
And meant to take his time,
For a fuck like this was fucking bliss,
So he played a pantomime.

He flicked his foreskin up and down,
His balls he did inflate,
'Till they looked like a couple of granite knobs
On top of a garden gate.
He winked his arsehole in and out,
His balls increased in size.
His mighty prick grew twice as thick
'Till it nearly reached his eyes.

He polished his knob with rum and gob
To make it steaming hot,
And to complete the job he sprinkled his knob
With the Cayenne pepper pot.
He didn't back or take a run, or make a flying leap,
He didn't stoop, but took a swoop
[But bent right down and came 'longside with]
And a steady forward creep.

Then he took his sight, as a gunman might,
along his mighty tool,
And showed his lust with a dextrous thrust,
Firm, calculating and cool.
[And the steady grin as he pushed it in was calculatedly cool.]

Have you seen the giant pistons working on the mighty CPR?
With a punishing force of ten thousand horse,
Then you know what pistons are.
[Or you think you do, but you've yet to learn
The ins and outs of the trick]

And now my friends it's time to learn of the awe-inspiring trick
And the work that's done on a non-stop run
By a man like Dead-eye Dick.

But Eskimo Nell was an Infidel
And equalled a whole harem,
With the strength of ten in her abdomen
And a rock of ages between.
Amidships she could stand the stream
Like the flush of a water closet
And she gripped his cock like the Chatswood lock
On the National Safe Deposit.

But Dead-eye Dick would not come quick,
He meant to reserve his powers.
If he'd mind he'd grind and grind
For a couple of solid hours.
Nell lay a while with a subtle smile
And the grip of her cunt grew keener,
'Till at last with a sigh she sucked him dry
With the ease of a vacuum cleaner.

She performed this feat [trick] in a way so neat [slick]
That it set in complete defiance.
The primary rules of classic schools
That govern sexual science.
[And the ancient rules of the Classic schools
In a moment or two went West].
She simply strode through the phallic code,
Which for ages had stood the test,
And with a movement quick she grabbed his prick
And made him give it a rest.

And now my friends we draw to the end
Of this copulative epic.
The effect on Dick was sudden and quick,
Akin to an anaesthetic.

He slipped to the floor and knew no more,
His passions extinct and dead,
Nor did she shout when his prick came out,
Though it certainly stripped the thread.

Then Mexican Pete jumped to his feet
To avenge his pal's affront
And with a jarring jolt of his blue-nosed Colt,
He jabbed it up her cunt.
He rammed it up to the trigger grip
And fired three times three,
But to his surprise she closed her eyes
And squealed in ecstasy.

With a movement neat she slipped to her feet
And cried out, "Bully for you.
[She jumped to her feet with a smile so sweet,
"Bully," she said, "For you"]
Though I might have guessed, it was the best
That you phoney lechers could do.
When next my friend you do intend
To have a bit of fun,
Get Dead-eye Dick a sugar stick
And yourself an elephant gun."

For I'm going back to the Frozen North,
Where a prick is hard and strong,
Back to the land of the mighty stand,
Where the nights are six months long.
It's as hard as tin when they put it in,
In the land where spunk is spunk,
Not a trickling stream of luke-warm cream,
but a solid frozen chunk.

Back to the land where they understand
What it means to fornicate,
Where even the dead sleep two in a bed
And infants copulate.
Back to the land of the mighty stand,

Where the nights are six months long,
Where the polar bear wanks off in his lair
That's where they'll sing this song.
[Back to the land of the grinding gland
Where the walrus plays with his prong.]

They'll tell this tale on the Arctic Trail
Where the nights are sixty below,
Where it's so damn cold, French letters are sold
Wrapped in balls of snow,
In the valley of death, with baited breath,
It's there we sing it too,
Where the skeletons rattle in sexual battle
And the mouldering corpses screw!

Back to the land where they understand
What it means to copulate,
Where even the dead share a double bed
And the children masturbate.
Back again to the land where men are men,
Terra Bollockium,
And now I'll go to the ice and snow
For the North is shouting "COME!"
[And there I'll spend my worthy end
For the North is calling "COME!"]

So Dead-eye Dick and Mexican Pete
Slunk out of the Rio Grande,
Dead-eye Dick with his useless prick
And Pete with no gun in his hand.

When a man grows old and his balls go cold
And the end of his cock turns blue,
And the hole in the middle refuses to piddle,
I'd say he was fucked, wouldn't you?

Little Mildred

Little Mildred based her hopes
On a book by Marie Stopes,
But to judge by her condition,
She must have bought the wrong edition.

All the prophylactics planned
Cannot rid this wicked land
Of the over-population
Caused by careless copulation.

All the choicest wares from France
Cannot beat the Laws of Chance.
We would rather trust to luck
And so enjoy an honest fuck.

Little Sally

Little Sally based her hopes,
On a book by Marie Stopes,
But to judge from her condition,
She must have bought the wrong edition.

All the sprays that ever whirled,
Cannot clean this wicked world,
Of the over-population,
Caused by careless copulation.

All the choicest goods of France,
Cannot beat the Laws of Chance,
Better by far to trust to luck,
And so enjoy an honest fuck.

The Second Oldest Profession

(Tune – The Vicar of Bray)

The Vicar of the village church to the Curate said for fun,
"I bet I've stuffed more boys than you," the Curate he said, "Done!"
"We'll stand outside the village church and this shall be our sign .
You say 'Ding Dong' to the boys you've done,
I'll say 'Ping Pong' to mine.
Ding Dong, Ding Dong, Ping Pong, Ping Pong,
There were more Ding Dongs than there were Ping Pongs.
When suddenly a nice boy came along
And the Curate said "Ping Pong",
Said the Vicar, "There's no 'Ping Pong' there,
It is my son I do declare",
"I don't give a bugger 'cos I've been there
With a Dinga Donga Dong Ping Pong."

Durex Is A Girl's Best Friend

(Tune – Diamonds are a Girl's Best Friend)

A poke with a bloke may be quite incidental,
Durex is a girl's best friend.
You may get the works,
But you won't be parental
As he slides it in,
You trust that good old latex skin.
As he lets fly, none gets by,
'Cos it's all gathered up in the end.
This little precuation
Avoids an abortion.
Durex is a girl's best friend.

Analysis of a Man

Men are what women marry. They have two hands, two feet and sometimes two wives, but never more than one pound or one idea at a time.

They are all made of the same material, like Turkish cigarettes, the only difference is that some are better disguised than others.

Generally speaking, they may be divided into three classes, husbands, bachelors and widowers.

A bachelor is an eligible man of obstinacy, entirely surrounded by suspicion.

Husbands are of three classes: prizes, surprises and consolation prizes.

Making a husband out of a man is one of the highest forms of plastic art known to civilisation. It requires science, sculpture, common sense, faith, hope and charity, mostly charity.

It is a psychological marvel that a small, tender, soft, violet-scented thing should enjoy kissing a big, awkward, stubble-chinned, tobacco and bay rum-scented thing like a man.

If you flatter him, you frighten him to death, if you do not, you bore him to death.

If you permit him to make love, he gets tired of you in the end. If you do not, he gets tired of you in the beginning.

If you believe everything he says, he ceases to be interested in you. If you argue with him in everything, you cease to charm him.

If you believe all he tells you, he thinks you are a fool. If you do not, he thinks you are a cynic.

If you wear gay colours, rough and startling hats, he hesitates to take you out, but if you wear a little brown beret and tailor-made suit, he takes you out and stares all evening at the women wearing gay colours and rough startling hats.

If you join in his gaieties and approve of his drinking, he swears that you are driving him to the devil. If you don't approve of his drinking and urge him to give up his gaieties, he vows you are a snob.

If you are the clinging vine type, he doubts whether you have a brain. If you are a modern, advanced, intelligent woman, he doubts whether you have a heart.

If you are silly, he longs for a bright mate. If you are brilliant and intelligent, he longs for a playmate.

Man is but a worm in the dust. He comes into the world, wriggles around for a while and finally some chicken gets him.

A Young Lady from Nantes

There was a young lady from Nantes,
Who was tres chic and elegante,
Her hole was so small it was no good at all
Except for la plume de ma tante.

Bollocks!

Where was the engine driver when the boiler burst?
Bollocks! They found his bollocks,
Ten thousand miles away.
Bollocks, they make a damn fine stew,
Bollocks, and the same to you!

They found one bollock ten thousand miles away,
Floating in the Hudson Bay,
His Mother found the other
When she was cleaning the kitchen grate.

The Farting Competition

Courtesy of Pat Murphy, Air Gunner. (Various versions merged).

I'll tell you a story that's certain to please,
Of a great farting contest at Shittam-on-Tees,
Where all the best arses paraded in fields
To take part in contests for various Shields.

Some tightened their arses to fart up the scale
To compete for a cup and a barrel of ale,
While others whose arses were biggest and strongest
Took part in the section for loudest and longest.

And the contest had drawn a very large crowd,
And the betting was evens on Mrs McLeod,
For 'twas said in the paper, the sporting edition,
That this woman's arse was in perfect condition.

Now old Mrs Brown was backed for a place,
For often she'd been placed in the deepest disgrace
For dropping a fart that had beaten the organ,
And gassed the poor Vicar the Reverend Morgan.

I found Mr Pothole was backed for a place
Though he's lately been placed in the deepest disgrace
For farting so loud he drowned the Church organ
And gassed the young Vicar and Choir-boy Morton.

Mrs McLeod had a perfect backside,
With a forest of hair and a wart on each side,
She fancied her chances of winning with ease,
Having trained on a diet of cabbage and peas.

Now young Mrs Bunghole, a maiden at farting
Was really a novice at competitive farting
And outsider of four in the farting display,
But she'd the prettiest arse you could see any day.

Mrs Bindle arrived midst roars of applause
And promptly proceeded to take down her drawers,
For though she'd no chance in the farting display,
She'd the prettiest arse you'd seen in a day.

The Vicar arrived and ascending the stand,
He proceeded to tell this remarkable band,
That the contest was on, as announced in the bills,
But the use was forbidden of injections or pills.

The Canon arrived and ascending the stand,
He addressed a few words to this gaseous band,
He read them the rules as displayed on the bills
Forbidding injections and usage of pills.

The ladies lined up at the signal to start
And winning the toss Mrs Jones took first fart.
The crowd were amazed mid silence and wonder,
The BBC broadcast gale warnings and thunder.

Old Mrs Jones then walked to the front
To proceed to show a remarkable stunt,
She took a deep breath and clenching her hands,
She lifted the roof off the sixpenny stands. [Royal Grandstands]

Mrs McLeod reckoned nothing of this,
She'd trained on weak tea and was all wind and piss,
With hands on her hips and legs stretched out wide,
She unluckily shit and was disqualified.

Young Mrs Bunghole was next to appear,
As she walked to the front, the crowd gave a cheer,
With her skirts lifted high she farted alone
And the crowd were amazed at the sweetness of tone.

This left Mrs Bindle who shyly appeared
And smiled at the clergy who lustily cheered
And though it was reckoned her chances were small,
She ran out a winner, out farting them all.

Next came Mrs Bingle who shyly appeared
And smiled on the crowd who lustily cheered.
They thought she was pretty, but no farting runt,
And most of the crowd wished to look at her cunt.

With muscles well tensed and legs well apart,
She farted a full and glorious fart,
Beginning with Chopin and ending with swing,
She went right up the scale, to "God Save the King."

Bawdy Ballads

With hands on her hips she stood farting alone,
And the crowd stood amazed at the sweetness of tone,
And the clergy agreed without hindrance or pause,
And said, "Now Mrs Bindle, please pull up your drawers."
(The judges agreed without stopping to think,
"First prize Mrs Bingle – oh she's starting to stink!")

She went to the rostrum with maidenly gait
And took from the Vicar a set of gold plate,
Then she turned to the Vicar with sweetness sublime,
And smilingly said, "Come up and see me sometime."

The Old Apple Tree

In the shade of the old apple tree,
A pair of fine legs I did see,
With some hairs at the top,
And a little red spot,
It looked like a cherry to me.

I pulled out my Pride of New York,
It fitted it just like a cork,
I said, "Darlin' don't scream,
While I dish out the cream,
In the shade of the old apple tree."

And as we both lay on the grass,
With my two hands round her fat arse,
She said, "If you'll be true,
You can have a suck too!
In the shade of the old apple tree!"

One of the Few

The Kentish sky's gentle blue
Ripped by savage tracery of white
And chattering death,
Faint heard by the farmer
Four miles below
Watching with anxious eye
The black plume of death.

The dying Knight
Coaxes his stumbling steed
With bloody hand.
His helmet, not of steel, but leather
Lolling on the Perspex
Of his belov'd machine
Spinning to oblivion.

His eyes fast glazing yet still see
His friends filling the pub
with youth and noise.
But most they see
His gold-haired girl.

His gold-haired girl, her body now
Shrine of a warrior's seed
Sown in whispered darkness
Of a summer's eve
In eagerness and fleeting joy
Yet lasting still in memory.

Her eyes bright with imminent tears
Unseeing now the telegram
Released from nervous hand
That flutters gently
To the ground.

One Fish Ball

There was a man strolled up and down
To see what he could find in town.
He came upon a gorgeous place
And entered in with modest grace.

He took his purse, his pocket hence
And found he had but fifteen cents,
He scanned the menu through and through,
To see what fifteen cents would do.

The only thing would do at all
Wa-wa-wa-wa-wa-wa-was one fish ball.
He called the waiter down the hall,
And softly whispered, "One fish ball."

The waiter bellowed down the hall,
"This gentleman here wants one fish ball."
The people stared both one and all,
To see who'd ordered one fish ball.

The wretched man felt ill at ease,
And softly whispered, "Bread, Sir, if you please."
The waiter bellowed down the hall,
"You'se get no bread with one fish ball."

There is a moral to it all,
"You'se get no bread with one fish ball!"

Twenty Toes

I know a game of twenty toes.
It's played all over town.
The girls play it with ten toes up,
The boys with ten toes down.

Albert

(Recitation)

I'll tell you a tale of young Albert,
Of when he came up for the Cup,
Of the things he did when in London,
And the doings to what he got up.

Now a randy young sod was our Albert,
And a grind was what he thought he'd like,
So he walked up and down Piccadilly,
With a truly phenomenal spike.

He saw some with faces all painted,
And some with a come hither look,
He thought, "ee I'd better be careful,
Cos it isn't their faces you fuck."

Then Albert walked up to a lady,
And said with a kind of a grin,
"Rhubarb's lovely this evening
And fair aches to be in".

At that she blushed and she simpered,
Her face went all of a flame,
"Do'est thou think I've never been slept wi'" says she,
"Nor taken men's money for shame?"

"Nay, nay, nay," says our Albert,
"I can see tha's a bit unskilled,
Let's say half a crown or a couple of bob,
Every time the letter is filled."

At that she got proper blazing,
As Albert fair could see,
"I'm senior tart on this street,
And thirty bob's my fee."

They argued the toss for an hour and a half,
And when they were set to begin,
The price they'd agreed on were twenty-five bob,
Wi' breakfast and letters thrown in.

Our Albert he ground himself stupid
And as he went on his way,
He thought with a grin of the grind he'd had,
And the breakfast he'd eaten that day.

That harlot were value for money,
She'd earned every bob of her pay,
And Albert contracted a fine dose of pox,
A keepsake for Cup Final Day.

The Walrus And The Carpenter

(Recitation)

If forty whores in purple dresses
Came walking down the Strand,
"Do you suppose," the Walrus said,
"A chap could raise a stand?"
"I doubt it," said the Carpenter,
"But wouldn't it be grand?"
And all the time,
The dirty swine was coming in his hand.

The Foggy Foggy Dew

(Tune as title)

I am a batchelor, I live by myself
And work at the weaver's trade,
The only thing I ever did wrong
Was to woo a fair young maid.

I wooed her in the Winter time
And in the Summer too,
And the only thing I ever did wrong
Was to save her from the foggy, foggy dew.

One night she came to my bedside,
Whilst I lay fast asleep.
She lay her head upon my bed
And she began to weep.

She cried, she sighed, she damned near died,
She said, "What shall I do?"
So I hauled her into bed and I covered up her head,
Just to save her from the foggy, foggy dew.

Now I am a batchelor but I have my son
And we work at the weaver's trade
And every time that I look into his eyes,
He reminds me of that fair young maid.

He reminds me of the Winter time
And of the Summer too
And the many, many times I held her in my arms,
To keep her from the foggy, foggy dew.

A Daily Prayer

Oh Lord help me keep my big mouth shut
Until I know what I'm talking about.
Amen

Those Foolish Things

(Tune as title)

A book of sex with fifty well-thumbed pages.
An old French letter that's been used for ages.
My penis hangs in strings!
These Foolish Things, remind me of you.

Remember Dear, that we talked of marriage.
That was the night you had your first miscarriage.
Abortions quite a few.
These foolish things remind me of you.

The newsboys calling out, "Late Night Final,"
The faint aroma of a gents' urinal,
Oh! How my penis stings!
These foolish things remind me of you.

The limp inertness of a used French letter
That I discarded when I knew you better:
A bed of creaking springs.
These foolish things remind me of you.

I came, you came, all over me
And in our ecstasy we simply knew that it had to be.
And in the bathroom on the morning after,
I saw your tits and how I howled with laughter,
Oh how the left one swings ...

The lumpy sofa that we had our shags on,
The smell that told me that you had your rags on.
Oh! How the memory clings!
These Foolish Things, remind me of you.

The price you charged me, dear, was sheer extortion,
I only wished to have myself a portion,
Not buy the fucking thing, your scabby ring,
Isn't worth a sou.

Frankie and Johnnie

(Tune as title)

Frankie and Johnnie were lovers,
Lordie how they could love,
Swore they'd be true to each other,
True as the stars above.
He was her man – but he done her wrong.

Frankie and Johnnie went walkin',
Johnnie in a brand new suit,
Frankie went walkin' with Johnnie,
Said, "Don't ma Johnnie look cute?
He is ma man – wouldn't do me no wrong."

Frankie went down to the corner,
Went for a bucket of beer,
Frankie said to the bartender,
"Has Johnnie, ma lover, been here?
He is ma man – wouldn't do me no wrong."

"Don't want to cause you no trouble,
Don't want to tell you no lie,
I saw Johnnie 'bout an hour ago,
With a girl called Nelly Bligh.
He is your man – but he done you wrong."

Frankie went down to the hotel,
She didn't go there for fun,
'Cos underneath her kimono
She toted a forty-four gun.
He was her man – but he done her wrong.

Frankie pulled back her kimono,
Pulled out the old forty-four,
Root-a-toot-toot, three times she shot,
Right through that hardwood door.
He was her man – but he done her wrong.

"Roll me over gently,
Roll me over slow,
Roll me over on my left side,
'Cos your bullets they hurt me so.
I was your man – but I done you wrong."

"Bring out your rubber-tyred hearses,
Bring out your rubber-tyred hack,
I'm taking ma lover to the graveyard,
And I ain't goin' to bring him back.
He was ma man – but he done me wrong."

Sheriff called the next morning,
Said it was all for the best,
He told her that Johnnie her lover
Was nothing but a doggone pest.
He was her man – but he done her wrong.

Frankie said to the Warden,
"What are they a'goin' to do?"
The Warden he says to Frankie,
"It's the electric chair for you.
He was your man – but he done you wrong."

This story ain't got no moral,
This story ain't got no end,
This story just goes to show,
That there ain't no good in men:
He was her man – but he done her wrong.

Three German Officers Crossed the Rhine

(Tune – Mademoiselle from Armentieres)

Three German Officers crossed the Rhine – *parlez-vous*,
Three German Officers crossed the Rhine – *parlez-vous*,
Three German Officers crossed the Rhine,
To fuck the women and drink the wine,
Inky-pinky parlez-vous.

They came unto a wayside inn – *parlez-vous*,
The cheeky buggers they walked right in.
(Shat on the mat and walked right in)
Inky, pinky, parlez-vous.

The Landlord had a daughter fair – *parlez-vous*,
With lily-white tits and golden hair.
Inky, pinky, parlez-vous.

My daughter, Sir, is much too young
To be fucked about by a son of a gun.
Inky, pinky, parlez-vous.

[Falsetto] Oh, Father dear, I'm not too young,
For I've been screwed by the Parson's son.
Inky, pinky, parlez-vous.

So up the stairs and into bed,
They fucked till she was nearly dead.
Inky, pinky, parlez-vous.

[At last they got her on a bed,
Shagged her till her cheeks were red,
Inky, pinky, parlez-vous.]

[And then they took her to a shed,
Shagged her till she was nearly dead,
Inky, pinky, parlez-vous.]

They took her to a shady lane,
Shagged her back to life again,
Inky, pinky, parlez-vous.

They shagged her up, they shagged her down,
They shagged her right around the town,
Inky, pinky, parlez-vous.

They shagged her in, they shagged her out,
They shagged her up her waterspout,
Inky, pinky, parlez-vous.

Seven months went and all was well,
Eight months went and she started to swell,
Inky, pinky, parlez-vous.

Nine months went, she gave a grunt
And a little white bastard popped out of her cunt,
Inky, pinky, parlez-vous.

The little white bugger he grew and grew,
He shagged his mother and his sister too,
Inky, pinky, parlez-vous.

The little white bugger he went to hell,
He shagged the Devil and his wife as well,
Inky, pinky, parlez-vous.

And now she's come to London Town,
And you can have her for half a crown.
Inky, pinky, parlez-vous.

Down by the Barrack Gate

At the call of the last trumpet,
Stood a little strumpet,
Down by the barrack gate.

Some Private from the kitchen,
Brought that dirty little bitch in,
Down by the barrack gate.

Said that martinet the Colonel,
"Damn my Soul in fires infernal,
The joys of fornication
Are for those of higher station,
It's the pastime of the great!"

But the Sergeant drill instructor
Took her down the road and fucked her,
Down by the barrack gate.

How that little harlot giggled
And her chubby arsecheeks wriggled,
For the Sergeant fucked like three men,
Spilling pints and pints of semen,
Down by the barrack gate.

But now his penis itches
In his Regimental britches
And he sheds an amber tear,
Sympathetic gonorrhoea,
Down by the barrack gate.

Grace

Her name was Grace, she was one of the best,
But that was the night I put her to the test,
I looked at her with gay delight,
For I knew that she was mine, all mine for the night.

She looked so pretty, so sweet, so slim,
The night was dark, the lights were dim,
I was so excited, my heart missed a beat,
For I knew I was in for a darned good treat.

I'd seen her stripped, I'd seen her bare,
I'd felt her all over, I'd felt everywhere,
Oh, that was the night I liked her best,
And if you will wait, I will tell you the rest.

I got inside her, she screamed with joy,
For this was her first night out with a boy,
I got up as high and as quick as I could,
And handled her gently, for she was so good.

I rolled her over on her side,
Then on her back I also tried,
She was one great thrill, the best in the land,
That twin-engined Mosquito of Bomber Command.

Grace #2

Oh! Darling Grace,
I love your face,
I love you in your nightie,
When the moonlight flits
Across your tits,
Oh! Jesus Christ Almighty!

Grandad's Grave

They're digging up Grandad's grave to build a sewer,
They're digging it up regardless of expense,
They're shifting his remains to build some shithouse drains,
Just to satisfy some nearby residents.
Cor Blimey!

Now what's the use of having a religion,
If when you die your troubles never cease,
'Cos some society twit wants a pipeline for a shit,
And will not let your bones lie there in peace.
Cor Blimey!

Now Grandad in his life was not a quitter,
I don't suppose he'd be a quitter now,
He'd dress up in a sheet and he'd haunt that shithouse seat,
And only let them shit when he allows.
Cor Blimey!

Now won't there be some awful constipation,
And won't the local people rant and rave,
It's only what they deserve for having the bloody nerve,
To muck about with a British Workman's grave.
COR BLIMEY!

An Aircrew Cadets' Lament

If I had the wings of a swallow
And the dirty great arse of a crow,
I would fly over hillock and hollow
And shit on the people below!

Father's Grave

a couple of variations

They're digging up Father's grave to build a sewer,
They're doin' this regardless of expense,
They're shovellin' his remains,
To make way for ten inch drains,
To ease the bums of some grand new residents.
Gor' Blimey.

Now what's the use of havin' a religion?
If when you're dead your troubles never cease?
'Cos some society squit,
Wants a pipeline for his shit,
They won't let poor old Father rest in peace.
Gor' Blimey.

Now Father in his life was not a quitter,
And I don't suppose he'll be a quitter now,
And in his grey grave sheet [and when the job's complete]
He'll haunt that shithouse seat,
So's they won't be pleased to crap there anyhow.
Gor' Blimey.

And Blimey!   Won't there be some constipation?
                    [Won't there be some fucking consternation]
And won't those richies rant and rave and shout?
                    [And won't those bleeding toffs just rant and rave]
And it'll serve them bloody right,
To have to bake their shite,
For fucking poor old Father's grave about!
Gor' Blimey!

Dual Control

Oh come with me my lady and together let us fly,
And I will teach you all I know when we are in the sky,
Though the Harvard may be grisly, I will try and make it do,
When I have a spot of dual control with you.

You'll learn exactly how (and what) to take off and perhaps,
You'll not feel too embarrassed when lowering your flaps,
There is one way up the runway I am anxious to pursue,
When I have a spot of dual control with you.

But when you're warmed up properly you'll realise the thrills,
Of lifting up your undercart and opening your gills,
You'll be purring to the whirring of my variable screw,
When I have a spot of dual control with you.

If when I flash my weapon you should do a barrel roll,
With the joystick in your cockpit you must exercise control,
For to get your carburettor flooded out would never do,
When I have a spot of dual control with you.

But if you think that all is lost then do not be a dunce,
Just call on Doctor Homer to prescribe for you at once,
So be clever dear and never let yourself get overdue,
When I have a spot of dual control with you.

The Balls of O'Leary

The balls of O'Leary are massive and hairy.
They're shapely and stately, like the dome of St Paul's.
People all muster to view the great cluster,
They stand and they stare
At the bloody great pair
Of O'Leary's balls.

The Valleys of Assam

I've crapped in the valleys of Assam,
I've pissed in the plains of Cawnpore,
I've often passed wind in the desert of Sind
And I've slept with a Calcutta whore.

I've belched near the Tropic of Cancer,
Stink-finger I've played in Madrid.
Put a girl in Bombay in the family way,
And refused to acknowledge the kid.

I've seduced little virgins in China,
I've taught self-abuse in Japan,
And when hard up for oats upon City Line boats,
I've had to resort to a man.

I've bathed in the nude in Llandudno,
I've fondled my foreskin out West,
And I've played soixante-neuf on Parisian turf
And I've belly-rubbed tarts in Trieste.

I've tickled the tits of a Nautch Girl,
I've French-kissed young women from Wales,
And I've played with my balls at Niagara Falls,
And I've been gamerouched in Marseilles.

I've split several arses in Karachi,
I've smacked bitches bums on the pier,
But what now fans the fire of my ardent desire
Is to bugger a goat in Kashmir!

The Hedgehog

(Recitation)

The exhaustive and careful enquiries
Of Darwin and Huxley and Ball,
Have conclusively proved that the hedgehog,
Can hardly be buggered at all.

But further most painful researches
Have incontrovertibly shown,
That this state of comparative safety
Is enjoyed by the hedgehog alone.

The sexual life of the camel
Is stranger than anyone thinks,
For at the height of the mating season,
He endeavours to bugger the sphinx.

But the Sphinx's posterior passage
Is blocked by the sands of the Nile,
Which accounts for the hump on the camel
And the Sphinx's inscrutable smile.

A Family Called Stein

There's a wonderful family called Stein,
There's Gert and there's Ep and there's Ein,
Gert's poems are bunk,
Ep's statues are junk,
And no one quite understands Ein.

The Hedgehog (Again!)

The carnal desires of the camel
Are stranger than anyone thinks.
This perverted and passionate mammal
Has designs on the hole of the Sphinx.

But the sphinx's posterior sphincter
Is clogged by the sands of the Nile,
Which accounts for the hump on the camel
And the sphinx's inscrutable smile.

In the process of syphilisation,
From the anthropoid ape down to man,
It is generally held that the Navy
Has buggered whatever it can.

Yet recent extensive researches
By Darwin and Huxley and Ball,
Conclusively prove that the hedgehog
Has never been buggered at all.

We therefore believe our conclusion
Has incontrovertibly shown,
That comparative safety on shipboard
Is enjoyed by the hedgehog alone.

Why haven't they done it at Spithead,
As they've done it at Harvard and Yale,
And also at Oxford and Cambridge
By shaving the spines off its tail?

My Husband

My husband is a plumber, a plumber, a plumber,
A very fine plumber is he.
All day long he screws pipes, he screws pipes, he screws pipes
And at night he comes home and screws me.

My husband is a farmer, a farmer, a farmer,
A very fine farmer is he.
All day long he ploughs furrows, he ploughs furrows,
he ploughs furrows
And at night he comes home and ploughs me.

My husband is a hunter, a hunter, a hunter,
A very fine hunter is he.
All day long he fox hunts, he fox hunts, he fox hunts
And at night he comes home and fox me.

My husband's a baker, a baker, a baker,
A very fine baker is he.
All day long he makes cakes, he makes cakes, he makes cakes
And at night he comes home and makes me.

My husband is a farmer, a farmer, a farmer,
And a very good farmer is he.
All day long he reaps crops, he reaps crops, he reaps crops
And at night he comes home and reaps me.

My husband's a miner, a miner, a miner,
And a very good miner is he.
All day long he drills rocks, he drills rocks, he drills rocks
And at night he comes home and drills me.

My husband is a mason, a mason, a mason,
A very fine mason is he.
All day long he lays bricks, he lays bricks, he lays bricks
And at night he comes home and lays me.

Bawdy Ballads

If

If you can keep your girl when all about you
Are losing theirs and blaming it on you:
And keep the faith of wives though husbands doubt you
And yet keep out of the Divorce Courts too.

If you can meet a girl and take her virtue,
Before you've had the time to learn her name,
And say to virgins, "This is going to hurt you,"
And yet go on and do it just the same.

If you don't hesitate when she says, "Maybe,"
And lead her on with every sort of lie,
And when she says she's going to have a baby,
Just quickly raise your hat and say, "Goodbye!"

If you can meet a new girl every minute
And not be faithful to a single one,
Yours is the world and every woman in it,
And, what is more, you'll be a cad my son.

When this Bloody War is Over

When this bloody war is over,
Oh, how happy I will be,
Take my kit bags to the station,
No more soldiering for me.

No more Church Parades on Sunday,
No more asking for a pass,
We will tell the Sergeant-Major,
To shove the passes up his arse.

My Jenny Wren Wedding

I've just come away from a Wedding,
And Lor' – I could laugh till I died.
I'll never forget the relations I met,
When I married my Jenny Wren Bride.

Her Father, he works in a dockyard,
Her Brother he owns a marine store,
And as for their habits, why talk about rabbits?
They've got half the dockyard ashore.

When I asked her Old Man for a dowry,
He gave me a drum of soft soap,
A bundle of waste and some polishing paste,
And fifty-two fathoms of rope.

The present we had from her Brother,
Was twenty-eight yards of Blue Jean:
Her Brother, the crusher, he gave us note-paper,
Six packets of "Service Latrine."

Her relations hung flags in the churchyard,
And painted the archway with flatting,
When along came the bride, they piped, "Over the side,"
And she tripped on the cocoanut matting.

Her wedding dress lashed up with spun yarn
Was made from an old cutter's sail,
On the top of her head a deck-cloth was spread
And a spud-net in front for a veil.

Her petticoat made of black hessian,
Her knickers cut out of green baize,
While for a suspender a motor-boat's fender
And two Purser's gaiters for stays.

The bulk of the congregation
Was made up of Wrens on the dole,
While asleep in the back pew was a six-inch gun's crew,
And half of the standing patrol.

The Parson strode up to the Altar
And asked, "Who gives this woman away?"
A bloke from the 'Hood' whispered, "Blimey! I could,
But let every dog have its day."

So now I'm just off on my Honeymoon,
I don't know what happens tonight,
But I've talked to a few who say that they do
And they swear she's a bit of alright!

Cuando Caliente El Sol

*Cuando caliente el sol a quien la playa
Ciento tu cuerpo vivrara a cerca de mi
Es tu palpitar son los ojos
Es tu pelo son tus besos
Me extremescos.*

*Cuando caliente el sol
A quien la playa
Ciento tu cuerpo vivrar cerca de mi
Es tu palpitar
Mi recuerdo
Mi lo cura
Mi delirio
Mi extremescos
Cuando caliente el sol.*

The Harlot of Jerusalem

(Various versions semi-merged)

Either   In Jerusalem there lived a maid,
           A maid who did a roaring trade,
           A prostitute of low repute,
           The Harlot of Jerusalem.

or   In days of old there lived a maid,
           She was the mistress of her trade,
           She did a roaring trade,
           The Harlot of Jerusalem.

CHORUS   *Hi, Hi, Cathusalem, Cathusalem, Cathusalem,*
           Hi, Hi, Cathusalem, the Harlot of Jerusalem.

This wily maid she had no fear
Of syphilis or pregnancies,
She kept it clear with gonorrhoea,
The pride of all Jerusalem.

Of pregnancy she had no fear,
'Cos she'd been fucked for many a year,
And sterilised by gonhorrhoea,
The Harlot of Jerusalem.

And though she fucked for many a year,
Of pregnancy she had no fear:
She washed her passage out with beer,
The best in all Jerusalem.

There lived a student by a wall,
Although he'd only got one ball,
He'd been through all, or nearly all,
The harlots of Jerusalem.

A student living by the Wall,
Although he only had one ball,
Resolved to do his very all,
To the Harlot of Jerusalem.

Now in a hovel by the wall,
A student lived with but one ball,
[Nearby there lived a bugger tall,
Who with his prick could break a wall]
Who'd been through all, or nearly all,
The harlots of Jerusalem.

His phallic limb was lean and tall,
His phallic art caused all to fall,
And victims lined the Wailing Wall
That goes around Jerusalem.

One night returning from a spree,
With customary cockstand he,
Although he'd only got 3 "d"
Accosted old Kathusalem.

One night, returning from a spree,
With customary jollity,
Although he only had 3d,
He accosted fair Cathusalem.

One night returning from a spree,
With customary whore-lust he,
Made up his mind to call and see
The harlot of Jerusalem.

It was for her no fortune good,
That he should need to root his pud,
And choose her out of all the brood
Of harlots of Jerusalem.

For though he paid his women well,
This syphilitic spawn of hell,
Struck down each year and tolled the bell
For ten harlots of Jerusalem.

Forth from the town he took the slut,
For 'twas his whim always to rut,
By the Salvation Army hut
Outside of Old Jerusalem.

With artful eye and leering look,
He took out from its filthy nook
His organ twisted like a crook,
The Pride of Old Jerusalem.

He leaned the whore against the slum
And tied her at her knee and bum,
Knowing where the strain would come
Upon the Fair Cathusalem.

She took the student to a nook,
Undid his flies and out she took,
His penis shaped just like a hook,
The pride of all Jerusalem.

She took him to a shady nook,
And from his trouser leg he took,
A penis like a reaping hook,
The pride of all Jerusalem.

He seized that harlot by the bum,
She rattled like a Lewis gun,
He sowed the seed of many a son
In the harlot of Jerusalem.

It was a sight to make you sick
To hear him grunt so fast and quick,
While rending with his crooked prick
The womb of Fair Cathusalem.

Then suddenly loomed up in sight
An Ismaelite, a fucking shite,
For he'd arranged to screw that night,
The Harlot of Jerusalem.

Along the shore there came a Knight,
An Israelite, a dirty shite,
Who had arranged to spend the night
With the Harlot of Jerusalem.

Then up there came an Onanite,
With warty prick besmeared with shite,
He'd sworn that he would gaol that night
The harlot of Jerusalem.

He loathed the act of copulation,
For his delight was masturbation,
And with a spurt of cruel elation,
He saw the whore Cathusalem.

So when he saw the grunting pair,
With roars of rage he rent the air,
And vowed that he would soon take care
Of the harlot of Jerusalem.

He grabbed the student by the crook,
And swearing by the Holy Book,
He held him o'er the Hebron brook
That flows by Old Jerusalem.

He grabbed the student by the crook,
And swearing by the Holy Book,
He cast him in the nearby brook
That flowed by Old Jerusalem.

Now this 'ere Wog he knew his stuff,
And he was plenty fucking tough,
He bent her over just enough,
And rammed his Hampton up her chuff.

The student came back full of fight
And grabbed that fucking Ismaelite,
And rammed him up with all his might
The arsehole of Cathusalem.

The student boy, he showed some fight,
He grabbed the shite, the Israelite,
And stuffed him up with all his might,
The arsehole of Cathusalem.

Upon the earth he found a stick,
To which he fastened half a brick,
And took a swipe at the mighty prick
Of the student of Jerusalem.

He seized the bastard by his crook,
Without a single furious look,
And flung him over Kedron's brook
That babbles past Jerusalem.

The student gave a furious roar
And rushed to even up the score,
And with his swollen cock did bore
The arsehole of Cathusalem.

And reeling full of a rage and fight,
He pushed the bastard Onanite,
And rubbed his face in Cathy's shite,
The foulest in Jerusalem.

The dirty pro she knew her part,
She closed her fan and blew a fart,
And sent the bastard like a dart,
High above Jerusalem.

Cathusalem, she played (knew) her part,
She closed her cunt (arse) and let a fart,
And shot the shite out like a dart,
Right over Old Jerusalem.

Away he soared right out to sea,
Just like a bloody bumble bee,
And left his bollocks on a tree,
Way up above Jerusalem.

And as the shite flew out to sea,
A'buzzing like a bumble bee,
His balls caught in a nearby tree,
That grows by Old Jerusalem.

And buzzing like a bumble bee,
He flew straight out towards the sea,
But caught his arsehole in a tree
That grows in Old Jerusalem.

Unto this day upon that tree,
His balls are there for all to see,
A warning there for you and me,
'Gainst the Harlot of Jerusalem.

And to this day you still can see
His arsehole hanging from that tree.
Let that to you a warning be
When passing through Jerusalem.

And when the moon is bright and red,
A castrated form sails overhead,
Still raining curses on the head
Of the harlot of Jerusalem.

As for the student and his lass,
Many a playful night did pass,
Until she joined the VD class
For harlots in Jerusalem.

On Ilkley Moor Bar t'at

Weer 'as tha bin sin' I saw thee?

On Ilkley Moor bar t'at,
On Ilkley Moor bar t'at,
On Ilk-ley Moor bar t'at – Tha twat!

Tha's bin an' caught tha death o' cold,
On Ilkley Moor bar t'at (etc)

Then we shall 'ave t' bury thee,
On Ilkley Moor bar t'at (etc)

Then t'worms'll coom an' eat thee oop,
On Ilkley Moor bar t'at (etc)

Then t'dooks'll coom an' eat oop t'worms,
On Ilkley Moor bar t'at (etc)

Then us'll coom an' eat oop dooks,
On Ilkley Moor bar t'at (etc)

Then us'll all'uv etten thee,
On Ilkley Moor bar t'at (etc)

Then us'll 'ave our own back.
On Ilkley Moor bar t'at (etc)

Little Jim

Now here's a pretty little song, so listen if you will,
About a little fellow born one night on Tooting Hill.
He was born on Tooting Hill my boys,
But spawned in Camberwell,
And when he popped out, he gave a shout,
"My Old Man fucked her well!"

Little Jim, content with masturbation,
Little Jim, playing with his tool,
Little Jim, content with simple frigging,
Thought a cunt was something you were called at public school.

Now down at Egham Manor there was a great ado,
For he buggered all the prefects and all the masters too,
But finally he was expelled, or so the records say,
For tossing off the Prince of Wales on Coronation Day.

Now Jenny was a whore in good old Cambridge Town,
Who had gamahuched the Proctor while he wore his cap and gown,
So his Uncle wrote to Jimmy saying, "Quick, and pack your things,
For the cunting season opens on the Twelfth at Kings."

His arrival at the 'Varsity was really quite grotesque,
For he laid his penis down upon the Tutor's desk,
Said his Tutor, "If the beastly thing drops off at an early date,
Please send it, I would like it as a special paper-weight."

Then he went to live with Milly, where he began to find,
That all his pals were queueing up for what they called "a grind,"
So down below the bed he lay despite the awful smell,
And every time a client came, young Jimmy came as well.

And Milly's all a landlord's daughter will or ought to be,
She rubs her cunt each morning while she drinks a cup of tea,
He's been through her so many times, the Magistrate declares,
That her vagina constitutes a legal thoroughfare.

Advice

Tell me friend John – do, if you can,
What is the reason, if a man
Attempts to take a Lady Fair,
By you know what, lies you know where,
That while he lives he still shall find,
The female, be she cross or kind,
Fret, frown, and push his hand away?
Tell me the reason: tell me pray.

Women still make a great pretence
To modesty and innocence.
And about virtue make a rout,
This is the reason, without doubt.

Listen! You shall the reason know:
Whene'er you thrust your hand below,
All women be they foul or fair,
Know that a hand is useless there:
But if from May to December,
You offer there the proper member,
Push as you will to give them pain,
They'll neither wince – nor yet complain.

Mary had a Little Lamb

Mary had a little lamb,
She also had a bear,
I've often seen our Mary's lamb,
But I've never seen her bare.

Mary had a little bear,
It followed her around,
And everywhere that Mary went,
She had a bare behind.

Keyhole in the Door

I left my girl quite early, 'twas hardly half past nine,
And by a stroke of bloody good luck, her room was next to mine.
Like Christopher Columbus, I started to explore,
I took up my position by the keyhole in the door.

CHORUS   *Keyhole, keyhole, keyhole, keyhole,*
                Keyhole in the door.
                I took up my position by the keyhole in the door.

My maid sat by the fireside, her dainty toes to warm,
She only had a chemise on to cover her lily-white form,
And if she took that chemise off I could not ask for more,
By Christ! I saw her do it through the keyhole in the door.

At last with trembling fingers I knocked upon the door,
And after much persuasion I crossed that threshold floor.
To stop some bastard seeing what I had seen before,
I stuffed that lily white chemise in the keyhole in the door.

That night I spent in Glory and other things besides,
And on her heaving bosom had many a joyful ride,
And when I woke next morning, John Tom was long and sore,
I felt as though I'd stuffed him through the keyhole in the door.

Sour grapes?

The Squadron Leaders and Wincos
And the Group Captains too,
Hands in their pockets and fuck-all to do,
Pinching the pay of the poor AC2,
May the Lord shit on them sideways,
May the Lord shit on them sideways.
Cried the Airmen, "Fuck you!"

Keyhole in the Door #2

I was invited for the weekend at a Ball at Cholmondely Hall
To celebrate the Wedding of Sue Vere and Cousin Paul.
I read the Guest List over and imagine my delight
When I found that Sweet Fanny Adams had come to spend the night!

Oh! The keyhole in the door, the door,
The keyhole in the door.
I took up my position by the keyhole in the door.

The Ball was one of splendour, all the City knobs were there,
Touching-up the ladies like farmers at the Fair
And Fanny fairly dazzled as she danced around the floor,
I resolved to lie in wait for her by the keyhole in the door.

I left the Ballroom early, just after half-past nine,
And as I hoped to find it, her room lay next to mine,
So taking off my trousers I set off to explore
And took up my position by the keyhole in the door.

I hadn't long to wait there wrapped in my dressing gown,
When I saw Fanny on the staircase retiring all alone.
She didn't lock her bedroom door, I couldn't ask for more,
And I crept out of the shadows by the keyhole in the door.

First she removed her stockings her silken legs to show
And then her frilly panties to reveal her furbelow.
"Now take off all the other things," was all I could implore
And silently I gripped the knob and crossed the threshold door.

Silently I shut the door and took her in my arms
And sooner than I'd expected discovered all her charms
And in case another person should see the sights I saw,
I hung her frilly panties o'er the keyhole in the door.

That night I rode in glory as I plumbed the girl's insides
And on her heaving belly I had many splendid rides,
But when I woke in the morning my tool was red and sore,
I felt that I'd been screwing through the keyhole in the door.

The Kidney Wiper

Once there was an Highland Tinker
Came all the way from France
Came all the way to England
To give Yank-bait a chance.

My Lady [A Duchess] was a-dressing
[The Lady of the Manor was]
A-dressing for a Ball,
When she espied a [the Highland] Tinker,
Pissing [tossing-off] against a wall.

CHORUS
With his bloody [fucking] great kidney wiper
And his balls as big as three
And half a yard of foreskin
Hanging down below his knee.
Hanging down! Swinging free!
And half a yard [forty yards] of foreskin
Hanging down below his knee.

My Lady [The Duchess] wrote a letter
And in it she did say,
She'd rather be fucked by a Tinker
Than by her Husband [His Lordship] any day.

The Tinker got the letter
And when it he did read,
His balls began to fester
And his prick began to bleed.

He mounted on his charger [donkey]
And on it he did ride,
His prick slung on his shoulder
And his bollocks [balls strapped] by his side.

He rode up to the Castle,
He strode into the hall.
"Cor Blimey!" ["Gawd Save us"] cried the Butler,
["Jesus!" wept the Footman,]
"He's come to fuck us all!"

He fucked the Cook in the kitchen
And the Housemaid in the hall
But the way he buggered the Butler,
Was the funniest fuck of all.

[He fucked 'em on the staircase
He fucked 'em in the hall,
But when he buggered the Butler,
'Twas the bloodiest trick of all!]
[He even fucked the tom-cat
As it scrambled up the wall.]

He fucked the Groom in the parlour
And the Duchess in her pew
But then he fucked the Gardener
And the Gardener's pet mole too.

At last he fucked the Lady
Against the bedroom door,
And judging by the size of it,
He thought she'd been a whore.

And now that the Tinker's dead, Sir,
And doubtless has gone to Hell,
He swore he'd fuck the Devil
And I'm sure he fuck'd him well.

The Ball of Kirriemuir # 1

At the Ball, at the Ball, at the Ball of Kirriemuir,
Half a hundred prostitutes a'coming o'er the Moor.

CHORUS   Singing, "I'll dee it this time, I'll dee it noo,
          Ye didna ha'e it last time, ye canna ha'e it noo."

Four and twenty virgins came down from Inverness,
But when the Ball was over, there were four and twenty less.

Maggie Thompson, she was there and she was dressed in blue,
They put her up against a wall and bulled her like a coo.

Farmer Brown, he was there and he lay down to grab,
For forty acres of his corn were fairly fucked down flat.

Maggie Brown, she was there, she had the place in fits,
By diving off the mantelpiece and landing on her tits.

The maid was in the stable, trying to teach the groom,
That the vagina, not the rectum, was the entrance to her womb.

The Sessions Clerk and he was there and he was black with ire,
He'd paid a wifie half a croon and found he couldna' fire.

The village grocer, he was there and was ashamed to see,
Four and twenty maidenheads a'hanging from a tree.

The village blacksmith, he was there, they had to put him oot,
For every time he farted, he filled the place with soot.

The doctor and the dairymaid went out to see the moon,
There'll be another bastard in the village verra soon.

The village postman, he was there, he had a dose of pox,
He couldn'a fuck the ladies so he stuffed the letter box.

There was fucking in the haystacks, fucking in the ricks,
You couldna' hear the music for the swishing of the pricks.

The village elders, they were there, a' sitting in a row,
A' counting up the pubic hairs and passing round a po.

The oldest inhabitant, he was there, he wasna' up to much,
He stuck the girls against the wall and poked them with his crutch.

The village parson, he was there, it was a crying shame,
He fucked a girl just eight years old, and wouldna' see her hame.

The village idiot, he was there, by Hell it was a farce,
He didna' know where to put it, so stuffed it up her arse.

The Wing Commander, he was there, he wore an awful froon,
He had his finger so far up, he couldna' get it doon.

Willie Thompson, he was there, he hid behind the byre,
Performing masturbation with an India rubber tyre.

There was fuckin' in the parlours, fuckin' on the stairs,
You couldna' see the carpet for the mass of curly hairs.

They were fucking in the bathroom, fucking on the stairs,
Ye couldnae see the carpet for the stronk and curly hairs.

The MT Officer, he was there, he took along his bride,
Who was fillin' out the 658s before he had a ride.

The Equipment Officer, he was there, he came in rather late,
He poked a whore with a 674 and came in triplicate.

The Intelligence Officer, he was there, he forgot to bring his cloak,
He stuffed his dagger up her arse and had a damned good poke.

The Medical Officer, he was there, wi' his bag of tricks,
And when the Ball was over, he sterilised the pricks.

The Medical Student, he was there, abortion was his trade,
And when the Ball was over, his fortune he had made.

There were Campbells, there were Camerons,
                              McDougals and O'Rourkes.
Ye couldnae see the barn floor for the bottoms wanting cocks.

And when the Ball was over, the lassies all confessed,
They thought the band was simply grand,
                              but the fuckin' was the best.

The Ball Of Kirriemuir #2

'Twas at the gatherin' of the Clans,
And all the Scots were there,
A'feelin' up the lassies,
Among the pubic hair.

CHORUS   *Singin' balls to your partner*
               Arse against the wall,
               If you can't get fucked this Saturday night,
               You'll never get fucked at all.

There was fuckin' in the haystacks, fuckin' in the ricks,
You couldna' hear the music for the swishin' o' the pricks.

The Undertaker, he was there, dressed in a long black shroud,
Swingin' from a chandelier and pissin' on the crowd.

The village cripple he was there, but didna' shag too much,
His old John Thomas had fallen off, so he fucked 'em wi' his crutch.

The local sweepie he was there a really filthy brute,
And every time he farted, he covered 'em all wi' soot.

The village idiot he was there, up to his favourite trick,
Bouncin' on his testicles and whistlin' through his prick.

The district nurse was there as well, she had us all in fits,
Jumpin' off the mantelpiece and landin' on her tits.

The village copper he was there, he had a dose of pox,
As he couldna' fuck the lassies, he stuffed the letter box.

The old fishmonger he was there, a dirty stinkin' sod,
He never got a stand that night, so he fucked 'em with a cod.

The local Vicar he was there, his collar back to front,
He said, "My girls thy sins are Blest," and shoved it up their cunts.

There was buggery in the parlour, sodomy on the stairs,
You couldna' see the dancin' floor for the mass of pubic hairs.

There was wee Dr Jameson, the one that fought the Boers,
He leaped up on the table and shouted for the whores.

Jock the blacksmith he was there, he couldna' play the game,
He fucked a lassie seven times and wouldna' see her hame.

The village elders they were there, and they were shocked to see,
Four and twenty maidenheads a hangin' fra' a tree.

The old schoolmaster he was there, he fucked by rule of thumb,
By logarithms he it worked out the time that he would come.

Four and twenty virgins, came down from Cuiremore,
Only two got back again and they were double bore.

In the mornin' early, the farmer nearly shat,
For twenty acres of his corn, were fairly fuckin' flat.

And when the ball was over, the maidens all confessed,
Although they liked the music, the fuckin' was the best.

various other verses

CHORUS   *Singing Fal dae it this time, fal dae it noo,*
          The one that did it last time, canna do it noo.

OR   *Balls to your father, arse against the wall,*
          If you've never been fucked on a Saturday night,
          You've never been fucked at all.

The Church Precentor he was there, he came in trews o' tartan,
They didna' like the colour but he said, "'Twas done by fartin'".

The village bobby he was there, he'd on his fancy socks,
He fucked a lassie forty times then found she had the pox.

The minister's wife, oh she was there, she was the best of a',
She stuck her arse agin the door and bad them come awa'.

The postie's daughter she was there, all draped up in the front,
Wi' poison ivy up her arse an' a thistle up her cunt.

The doctor's wife, oh she was there, she wasna' very weel,
For she had to mak her water in the middle o' a reel.

The butcher's wife, oh she was there, she also wasna' weel,
For she had to go and piddle after every little feel.

Jock McGregor he was there, in a new Ford truck,
They asked if he'd have a dram but he said he'd rather fuck.

Roon about the washin' hoos and in among the ricks,
Ye couldna' see a blade o' grass for balls and standin' pricks.

Mr McFudge the parson, he went among the women,
He took puir Nellie on his knee and filled her full of semen.

John Broon the factor, he didna' think it shame,
To dance a bloody hornpipe upon a lassie's wame.

The village loony he was there, he was an awful ass,
He went into the granary and stuffed his arse wi' grass.

Farmer Tampson, he was there, he sat doon and grat,
For forty acres of his oats were fairly fuckit flat.

There was fuckin' in the barnyard and fuckin' in the laft,
But one auld wife of eighty-five was nic't against the shaft.

Jean McPherson, she was there, she cowped wi' a dunt,
And all the folk rejoiced to see her muckle hairy cunt.

First lady forward, second lady back,
First lady's finger up the second lady's crack.

Little Willie, he was there, he was only eight,
He couldna' fuck the women, so he had to masturbate.

The teacher fra' the school was there, she didna' bring her stick,
She wasna' much to look at, but could she take the prick.

The village blacksmith, he was there, he was a mighty man,
He had two balls between his legs that rattled as he ran.

The King was in the counting house, counting up his wealth,
The Queen was in the parlour, a-playin' wi' herself.

Jock McBride, he was there, a-sittin' on a stool,
Three of the legs were wooden, the fourth was his tool.

The village vicar, he was there, to fuckin' wouldna' stoop,
They say he's keen on buggery since he joined the Oxford Group.

The vicars daughter, she was there, a lousy little runt,
Wi' roses round her arsehole and barbed wire round her cunt.

The village pro was there as well, up to her usual tricks,
Swingin' fra' the chandeliers and landin' on men's pricks.

Now Mrs Steward, she was there, she was the worst of all,
In the bed, oot the bed, up against the wall.

The grocer's wife, she was there, she had a novel stunt,
Poison ivy round her neck, a carrot up her cunt.

The Intelligence Officer, he was there frigging in the hay,
Feeling in his pockets for the letter of the day.

And when the ba' was over, the ladies all expressed,
They'd all enjoyed the dancin', but the fuckin' was the best.

And noo the ba' is over, and a' are on their ways,
Excepting Meg McPherson who's comin' through her stays.

Yet ANOTHER version!

The Ball, the Ball of Kirriemuir, the Ball of Kirriemuir,
Where your wife and my wife were a'doing on the floor.

CHORUS   *Singing who'll do it this time, who'll do it noo?*
          The one that did it last time will no a 'do it noo.

Four and twenty prostitutes came down from Glockamore,
And when the ball was over they were all of double bore.

The village plumber he was there, he felt an awful fool,
He'd come eleven leagues or more and forgot to bring his tool.

There was fucking in the hallways and fucking in the ricks,
You couldn't hear the music for the swishing of the pricks.

There was fucking in the kitchen and fucking in the halls,
You couldn't hear the music for the clanging of the balls.

There was fuckin' in the parlours, fuckin' on the stairs,
You couldna' see the carpet for the mass of curly hairs.

The vicar's wife, well she was there, a'sitting by the fire,
Knitting rubber Johnnies out of India-rubber tyres.

The village magician, he was there, up to his favourite trick,
Pulling his arsehole over his head and standing on his prick.

The village smithy he was there a'sitting by the fire,
Doing abortions by the score with a piece of red-hot wire.

The blacksmith's brother he was there, a mighty man was he,
He lined them up against the wall and fucked them three by three.

Now farmer Giles he too was there, his sickle in his hand,
And every time he swung around he circumcised the band.

The vicar's wife she too was there, her back against the wall,
"Put your money on the table boys, I'm fit to do you all."

The vicar and his wife were having lots and lots of fun,
The parson had his finger up another lady's bum.

Father O'Flannagan he was there and in the corner sat,
Amusing himself by abusing himself and catching it in his hat.

Giles he played a dirty trick, we canna let it pass,
He showed a lass his mighty prick and shoved it up her arse.

Dino had an even stroke, his skill was much admired,
He gratified one cunt at a time until his prick expired.

Lindsay Bedogni he was there and he was in despair,
He couldna get his prick through all the tangles of her hair.

Jockie Stewart did his fucking up upon the moor,
It was, he thought, much better than fucking on the floor.

Jock McVenning he was there a'looking for a fuck,
But every cunt was occupied and he was out of luck.

Mike McMurdoch when he got there his prick was long and high,
But when he'd fucked her forty times his balls were mighty dry.

Mactavish oh yes he was there, his prick was long and broad,
And when he'd fucked the furrier's wife she had to be rebored.

McCardew-Roberts he was there, his prick was all alert,
But when half the night was done,'twas dangling in the dirt.

The village doctor, he was there, a black bag in his hand,
Gently masturbating to the rhythm of the band.

The doctor's daughter she was there, she went to gather sticks,
She couldna' find a blade of grass for cunts and standing pricks.

The village builder he was there, he brought his bag of tricks,
He poured cement in all the holes and blunted all the pricks.

The blacksmith's father he was there a'roaring like a lion,
He'd cut his prick off in the forge so he used a red-hot iron.

And when the ball was over, eveyone confessed,
They all enjoyed the music, but the fucking was the best.

And when the ball was over, they all went home to rest,
The music had been exquisite, but the fucking was the best.

AND MORE!

The ball, the ball, the ball, the ball, the ball at Kirriemuir,
Where four and twenty prostitutes came dancing through the door.

Singing "Who'll do it this time and who'll do it noo?
The man who did it last time he canna do it noo."

And when the Ball it started they all began to jig,
Before half an hour had passed, they all began to frig.

First lady forward, second lady back,
Third lady's finger up the fourth lady's crack.

Fifth lady curtsy, sixth lady pass,
Seventh lady's finger up the eighth lady's arse.

There was fookin' in the highways and fookin' in the lanes,
Ye couldn't hear the music for the semen in the drains.

So here's to guid auld Kirriemuir
And to its famous ball.
I cannae sing another verse,
I'm just about tae fall.

Lady Jane

It nearly broke her Father's heart
When Lady Jane became a tart,
But blood is blood and race is race,
And so to save the family face
He bought her quite the nicest beat
On the shady side of Jermyn Street.

Her Father's strict regulations
Regarding all her copulations
No balls could nestle with her charms
Unless they bore a Coat of Arms
No prick could ever hope for entry
Unless it came of Landed Gentry.

And so her fame began to swell
A vast exclusive clientele.
'Twas even rumoured, without malice,
She had a client at the Palace,
And long before her sun had set,
She'd fucked her way right through Debrett.

It hardly took poor Father's fancy
When Brother Claude became a Nancy.
He thought their friends would all neglect'em
If common chaps used young Claude's rectum,
So Claude swore he'd hawk his steerage
Exclusively amongst the Peerage.

Her Ladyship, abandoning caution,
Then gave classes in abortion.
Her Daughter, her first patient, died.
She spent the next two years inside.
Poor Father, feeling rather limp
Regretfully became a pimp.

Pump Away

Oh, once I had a girl, had a girl,
Oh, once I had a girl, had a girl,
Oh, once I had a girl, put me in a whirl.
Put your shoulder next to mine
And pump away, pump away,
Put your shoulder next to mine
And pump away.

She had me on a string
And I bought her everything.

When I came home from sea,
I bought her gifts so free.

I bought her presents one,
She said I shouldn't have done.

I bought her presents two
And her heart she let me woo.

I bought her presents three
And she caught me by the lee.

I bought her presents four
And she met me on the shore.

I bought her presents five
And she was very much alive.

I bought her presents six
And that one did the trick.

I bought her presents seven
And she said she was in heaven.

I bought her presents eight
And I took her for my mate.

I bought her presents nine
And the baby's doing fine.

I bought her presents ten,
And she said, "Let's start again."

They Say There's A ... Just Leaving

(Tune – Bless 'em all) *The original version belonged to the RNAS but was later taken over by the RAF*

They say there's a [Hali/Lanc/etc] just leaving,
Bound for old Blighty's shore,
Heavily laden with terrified men, shit scared and flat on the floor.
They say there are Messerschmitts pumping in lead,
They say there are 190s too,
They shot off our bollocks and fucked the hydraulics,
So cheer up my lads, fuck 'em all.

Fuck 'em all, fuck 'em all,
The long and the short and the tall,
Fuck all the Sergeants and WO1s,
Fuck all the Corporals and their bastard sons,
For we're saying goodbye to them all,
As up the CO's arsehole they crawl,
You'll get no promotion this side of the ocean,
So cheer up my lads, fuck 'em all.

With six QDMs and some fucking good luck
We get back to Blighty's shore.
The cloud was 11/10ths right on the deck,
In fact 'twas a fucking sight more.
In ten fucking years when they're digging for coal
In a bloody great hole close to Wick,
They'll dig up a ... two beds and a shitehawk,
So cheer up my lads, fuck 'em all.

The other poor bastards who fell in the shit,
They sent them to ...
The runway was 90 degrees out of wind,
It tried fucking hard to be more.
Now Coastal Command think this is fucking good fun,
They chortle like bastards and say,
"We'll get no promotion this side of the ocean
If 899 fly every day."

These fucking controllers are driving me mad,
They don't know a map from a chart,
They think that a shitbag's a bag full of shit,
A wind lane the track of a fart,
They think that a sextant's a man of the Church,
A bearing a little steel ball.
We talk about bombsights – they think we're three parts tight,
'Cos a bombsight's got no eyes at all.

Letitia has a Large One

Letitia has a large one and so has Cousin Luce.
Eliza has a small one, though large enough for use.

Beneath a soft and glossy curl, each Lass has one in front.
To find one in an animal, you at the tail must hunt.

A child may have a little one enclosed within a clout,
In fact all females have one, no girl is born without.

All fowls have one (not cocks of course) and though prolific feeders,
The fact that fish have none at all is known to piscine breeders.

Hermaphrodites have none, Mermaids are minus too,
Nell Gwyn, possessed a double share if books we read are true.

It's used by all in Nuptual Bliss, in Carnal Pleasures found.
Destroy it, Life becomes extinct: the world is but a sound.

Lasciviousness here has its source, Harlots its use apply.
Without it Lust has never been and even Love would die.

Now tell me what this wonder is, put pause before you guess it.
If you are Mother, Maid or Man, I swear you don't possess it.

Answer? The Letter "L".

Lilian Barker

Although a lady of ill repute,
Lilian Barker was a beaut,
And it was really deemed an honour
To be allowed to climb upon her.

Her lovely face was smooth and fair
And golden was her flowing hair,
Yet pot and hash and cruel cocaine
Had ravaged heart and Soul and brain.

Lil could take with sly content
A Trooper of his Regiment.
Hyperbole it sometimes seems
Is not confined to wishful dreams.

But soon she had to see a doctor
To find out what disease had pocked her.
The diagnosis short and clear
Revealed a dose of gonorrhoea.

As Lilian lay in her disgrace,
She felt the devil kiss her face.
She said, "Now Mate, I'm always willing,
But first let's see your silver shilling."

Alice Tucker

(Tune – The Road to the Isles)

There's a man that sits in prison,
With his hands upon his knees,
And the shadow of his penis on the wall:
And the hairs go flicker-flacker,
From his arsehole to his knacker,
And the rats are playing croquet with his balls.
[And the ladies as they pass, stick their hat-pins up his arse
And the little mice play billiards with his balls.]

There's a Gentleman's urinal,
To the North of Waterloo,
There's a Ladies just a little further down.
There's a constipated woman,
Putting pennies in the slot,
While the attendant stands and watches with a frown.

[There's a smelly men's urinal
To the North of Waterloo.
There's another one for women further down.
There's a girl called Alice Tucker
And for sixpence you can fuck her
You can sleep with her all night for half a crown.]

Tho' she's known as Alice Tucker
By the dirty sods who fuck her,
Her proper name is Carolina Black.
She was thrown out by her Father
'Cos she had a dose of clap
And now she makes a living on her back.

She's the dirtiest of bitches,
By the colour of her breeches,
You would think that she'd never had a wash.
But the juice from her vagina
Was considerably finer
Than the most expensive gin and orange squash.

Bawdy Ballads

The Chastity Belt

Oh! Pray gentle maiden, let me be your lover,
Condemn me no longer to mourn and to weep.
Struck down like a hart, I lie bleeding and panting
Let down your drawbridge, I'll enter your keep.
Enter your keep, nonny, nonny,
Enter your keep, nonny, nonny,
Let down your drawbridge, I'll enter your keep.

Alas gentle errant, I am not a maiden,
I'm married to Sir Oswald, the cunning old Celt,
He's gone to the wars for a twelve month or longer
And taken the key to my chastity belt.

Fear not, gentle maiden, for I know a locksmith.
To his forge we will go: on his door we will knock
And try to avail us of his specialised knowledge
And see if he's able to unpick your lock.

Alas, Sir and Madam, to help I'm unable,
My technical knowledge is of no avail.
I can't find the secret of your combination.
The cunning old bastard has fitted a Yale.

I'm back from the wars with sad news of disaster,
A terrible mishap I have to confide.
As my ship was a passing the Straits of Gibraltar,
I carelessly dropped the key over the side.

Alas and alack, I am locked up for ever.
Then up stepped the page-boy saying, "Leave this to me:
If you will allow me to enter your chamber
I'll open it up with my duplicate key".

Lulu

Some girls work in factories, some girls work in stores,
But Lulu works in a knocking shop, with forty other whores.

My Lulu was a lady who came from a country town,
She kept her reputation up, but she couldn't keep her skirt tail down.

CHORUS   *Bang it into Lulu, bang it good and strong,*
             Oh what shall we do for a good blow through
             When Lulu's dead and gone?
             So bang away at Lulu, bang her good and strong,
             For what shall we do for banging
             When Lulu's dead and gone?

My Lulu was a lady who was free from care and sin,
I caught her once on a railway track, jerking off with a coupling pin.

Lulu took me walking into a field of corn
I lay my Lulu on the ground and got a bloody great horn.

The next field that we came to, it was a field of rye,
I lay my Lulu on the ground and shot right in her eye.

My Lulu was a lady, she married Sonny Jim,
She got mad with the son-of-a-bitch and pissed all over him.

My Lulu had a baby, she named him after Jim,
[Lulu had a baby, she called it Sonny Jim,]
And put him in a pisspot to see if he could swim.

First he went to the bottom, then he came to the top,
Lulu screamed and lost her head and grabbed him by the cock.

Lulu had a baby, it was an awful shock,
She couldn't call it Lulu 'cos the bastard had a cock.

I took her to the pictures, we sat down in the stalls,
And every time the lights went out she grabbed me by the balls.

She and I went fishing in a dainty punt
And every time I hooked a sprat, she stuffed it up her cunt.

I wish I were a wedding ring upon Lulu's hand,
And every time she wiped her arse, I'd see the promised land.

I wish I were a pisspot under Lulu's bed,
For every time she pissed I'd see her maidenhead.

The rich girl uses vaseline, the poor girl uses lard,
Lulu uses axle grease and gets it twice as hard.

Oh! A rich girl's watch is made of gold and a poor girl's is of brass.
Lulu has no watch at all, but the movement of her arse.

Lulu joined the WRNS, they sent her to the front,
It wasn't the lead that killed them dead, but the smell of Lulu's cunt.

Honolulu Penny

Q   *What is the difference between a Honolulu Penny
        and an English one?*

A   *It's on her Lulu.*

Why?

I often think, dear God why
Did all those men go out to die?
Their blood soaked up into the sand
Fighting in a foreign land.

In my thoughts I see them still,
Snowy, Taffy, Knocker, Bill,
Jack Cowie and Jock Sutherland
And all my other mates so grand.

Lydia Pink

(Tune as title)

CHORUS   *We'll drink a drink, a drink, a drink,*
            To Lydia Pink, a Pink, a Pink,
            The Saviour of the Human Race.
            She invented a vegetable compound
            Efficacious in every case.

Mr Brown had a very small penis,
And he could hardly raise a stand,
So they gave him some of the compound,
Now he comes in either hand.

Now Master Brown had very small knackers,
They were just like a couple of peas,
So they gave him some of the compound,
(Bass voice)And now they hang below his knees.

Now Mrs Brown had very small bosoms,
They hardly showed beneath her blouse,
So they gave her some of the compound,
And now they milk her, just like the cows.

Mrs Jones had a very bad stricture
She could hardly bear to pee,
So they gave her some of the compound,
Now they pump her direct to sea.

Mrs Green was having a baby,
And the pain it was hard to bear,
So they gave her some of the compound,
Now she's having it over a chair.

Mrs Black had a very tight grummet,
And could hardly pee at all,
So they gave her some of the compound,
Now she's like Niagara Falls.

Bawdy Ballads

Uncle Dick and Auntie Mabel

(Tunes – Hark the Herald Angels Sing)

Uncle Dick and Auntie Mabel
Fainted at the breakfast table.
This should be a solemn warning
Not to do it in the morning.

Uncle Ted has much improved
Since he had his balls removed,
Not only has he lost desire,
He now sings treble in the choir.

At a party, little Dick
Shouted, "Someone suck my prick!"
Women fainted, strong men shuddered,
Father said, "Well I'll be buggered!"

Little Francis home from school
Picked up baby by the tool,
Nurse said, "Now Master Francis,
Don't spoil baby's fucking chances."

Little Miss Muffet sat on a tuffet,
Her knickers all tattered and torn,
It wasn't a spider that sat down beside her,
But Little Boy Blue with his Horn.

The Benghazi Mail Run

70 Squadron (Tune – Clementine)

Take off for the Western Desert
Fulka 60 or 09
Same old Wimpey, same old target,
Same old Aircrew, same old time.

CHORUS   *Seventy Squadron, Seventy Squadron,*
                  Though we say it with a sigh,
                  Must we do this ruddy Mail Run,
                  Every night until we die?

"Have you lost us Navigator?
Come up here and have a look,
Someone's shot the starboard wing off,
We're alright then, that's Tobruk."

Forty Wimpeys on the target,
Two were ditched down in the drink,
Then three others crashed on landing,
Bloody Hell! It makes you think.

Stooge on around the Western Desert,
With the gravy running low,
How I wish I could see Fuka
Through the sandstorm far below.

First it's Derna, then it's Barce,
Even IQ isn't sure,
They've changed the bomb load twice already,
It's a proper Cookies tour.

All this flapping cannot fool us,
We know just where we have to be,
Rumour's heard of a new target,
But after all it's just B G.

"To Benghazi," is the slogan,
We'll take the load right through once more,
So start your engines, let's get cracking,
The Mail Run's going as before.

Intelligence tells us from his photographs,
We never hit a single flea,
Sees no bombholes in the rooftops,
Only craters in the sea.

He asks us if we're sure we pranged it,
Must have been some other spot,
Suggests we bombed a dummy target,
Never heard such bloody rot.

Try to get a tour of ops in
Without your aircraft being hit,
If you do, you'll go to Blighty,
If you don't you're in the pit.

Oh! To be in Piccadilly
Selling matches by the score,
Then we wouldn't have to do this
Bloody Mail Run any more.

Dirty Gertie

Dirty Gertie from Bizerte
Hid a mousie beneath her skirtie,
Made her boyfriends' fingers hurtie.
She was voted in Bizerte,
Miss Latrine for 1930.

Malaya

(Tune – Only a Bird in a Guilded Cage)

I'll tell you of a place in Malaya,
Butterworth is its name,
It's the worst fucking place in Malaya,
It's the worst fucking place on Earth.

There were whore bags and cow bags and shit bags
And bags of Gonhorrhoea
And the Nurse as she pulled back my foreskin,
She whispered these words in my ear.

"If these lips could only speak,
And those eyes could only see,
And those horrible bags that you went through,
Were here in reality.

But alas you came unstuck,
And your knob is all bunged up,
Never again will you go for,
A two dollar fifty cent fuck."

Tiger Lil

With arms akimbo, there stands Tiger Lil,
Her great big quim you'll find hard to fill.
She'll grab your akkers, then shout out with glee,
"Come all you Air Crew Queens, abide with me".

My Love Is For A Bold Marine

A miner coming home one night,
Found his house without a light
And as he went upstairs to bed,
A strange thought came into his head.

He went into his daughter's room
And found her hanging from a beam.
He took his knife and cut her down,
And on her breast this note he found.

"My love is for a bold Marine,
I always, always, think of him,
And though he's far across the sea,
He never, never, thinks of me!

So all you maidens bear in mind,
A good man's love is hard to find.
Dig my grave both wide and deep,
And rest my weary bones in sleep."

They dug her grave both wide and deep
And laid white lilies at her feet.
On her breast a turtle dove,
To signify she died of love.

Diamond Lily

"Oh my name is Diamond Lily,
I'm a whore in Piccadilly,
And my Father runs a brothel in the Strand,
And my Brother sells his arsehole,
To the Guards at Windsor Castle:
We're the finest fuckin' family in the land."

If I Were The Marrying Kind

(Tune – One Man Went to Mow)

If I were the marrying kind
Which I thank the Lord I'm not Sir,
The kind of man that I would wed
Would be a Rugby Full Back.

And he'd find touch and I'd find touch,
We'd both find touch together,
We'd be all right in the middle of the night
Finding touch together.

If I were the marrying kind
Which thank the Lord I'm not Sir,
The kind of man that I would wed
Would be a Wing Three-quarter.

And he'd go hard and I'd go hard,
We'd both go hard together.
We'd be all right in the middle of the night,
Going hard together.

If I were the marrying kind
Which thank the Lord I'm not Sir,
The kind of man that I would wed
Would be a Centre Three-quarter.

And he'd pass it out and I'd pass it out,
We'd both pass it out together,
We'd be all right in the middle of the night,
Passing it out together.

If I were the marrying kind
Which thank the Lord I'm not Sir,
The kind of man that I would wed
Would be a Rugby Fly-half.

And he'd whip it out and I'd whip it out,
We'd both whip it out together,
We'd both be all right in the middle of the night,
Whipping it out together.

If I were the marrying kind
Which thank the Lord I'm not Sir,
The kind of man that I would wed
Would be a Rugby Scrum-half.

And he'd put it in and I'd put it in,
We'd both put it in together,
We'd be all right in the middle of the night,
Putting it in together.

If I were the marrying kind
Which thank the Lord I'm not Sir,
The kind of man that I would wed
Would be a Rugby Hooker.

And he'd strike hard and I'd strike hard,
We'd both strike hard together,
We'd be all right in the middle of the night,
Striking hard together.

If I were the marrying kind
Which thank the Lord I'm not Sir,
The kind of man that I would wed
Would be a Big Prop-forward.

And he'd bind tight and I'd bind tight,
We'd both bind tight together,
We'd be all right in the middle of the night,
Binding tight together.

If I were the marrying kind
Which thank the Lord I'm not Sir,
The kind of man that I would wed
Would be a Referee.

And he would blow and I would blow,
We'd both blow together,
We'd be all right in the middle of the night,
Blowing hard together.

Mary Was A Good Girl

(Recitation – various variations)

Mary was a good girl [servant girl],
She lived down Drury Lane,
Her mistress she was good to her [was a drunkard]
Her master was the same.

Early one evening a Sailor came to tea,
And here was the beginning of Mary's misery,
He asked her for a candle to light him up to bed,
He asked her for a pillow on which to lay his head.

Mary very foolish, and thinking it no harm,
Got in beside him, to keep the Sailor warm,
He laid her over gently and turned her on her back,
Get in there nobby, never mind the heavy flak.

Early next morning the Sailor he awoke,
And extracted from his pocket a dirty five pound note,
"Take this darlin' for the damage I have done,
I am leaving you in charge of a daughter or a son."

"Now if it be a daughter, then lay her on her back,
                     [nurse her on your knee],
And if it be a son, send the bastard off to sea,
Bell bottom trousers and a coat of Navy Blue,
Let him climb the rigging just as I climbed up you."

Now Mary up with piss-pot and chucked it at his head,
"Take that you dirty bastard for fucking me in bed,"
She also spied a shotgun and shot his balls right through,
"Take that you low down bastard for giving me a screw."

Now all you young servant girls, listen to my plea,
Never let a Sailor one inch above your knee.
'Cos if you do my darling, he will never rest,
'Till he gets his masthead into your old crows' nest!

Walking in a Meadow Green

Walking in a meadow green,
Fair flowers for to gather,
Where primrose ranks did stand on banks
To welcome comers thither.
I heard a voice which made a noise,
And caused me to attend it,
I heard a lass say to a lad,
"Once more and none can mend it!"

They lay so close together,
They made me much to wonder,
I knew not which was whether,
Until I saw her under.
Then off he came and blushed for shame,
So soon that he had ended:
Yet still she lies and to him cries,
"Once more and none can mend it!"

His looks were dull and very sad,
His courage she had tamed:
She bade him play the lusty lad,
Or quit and be ashamed.
"So stiffly thrust and hit me just,
Fear not, but freely spend it,
Come, play about, now in – now out,
Once more and none can mend it!"

At last he thought to enter her,
Thinking the horn was on him:
But when he came to enter her,
The point turned back upon him.
She said, "O stay! Go not away,
Although the point be bended!
But plunge again, and hit the vein!
Once more, and none can mend it!"

Then in her arms she did him fold,
And oftentimes she kissed him,
Yet still his courage was but cold,
For all the good she wished him.
With her white hand she made it stand,
So stiff she could not bend it,
And then anon she cried, "Come on
Once more, and none can mend it!"

"Adieu, adieu, sweetheart," said he,
"For in faith I must be gone."
"Nay, then you do me wrong," quoth she,
"To leave me thus alone."
Away he went when all was spent,
And she was most offended:
Like a Trojan True, she made a vow,
She'd soon have one to mend it!

Cold

Cold as a frog in an ice-bound pool,
Cold as the end of an Eskimo's tool,
Cold as a rat in a frozen sewer,
Cold as the heart of a worn-out whore,
Cold as the love of a man who can't come,
Cold as the hairs round a polar bear's bum,
Cold as Charity and that's pretty chilly,
But not half as cold as our poor Willie,
'Cos he's dead, poor bugger.

In Mobile

(Various versions semi-merged)

In some versions 'shite-hawks' replaced by 'eagles'
(Sometimes 'Mobile' replaced by 'Matruh')

Oh, the shite-hawks they fly high in Mobile,
Oh, the shite-hawks they fly high in Mobile,
Oh, the shite-hawks they fly high
And they shit right in your eye,
It's a good thing cows can't fly, in Mobile.

There's a shortage of good whores in Mobile,
But there's key-holes in the doors,
And there's knot-holes in the floors, in Mobile.

It's a habit of the working classes [upper classes] in Mobile,
When they've finished with their glasses,
To stick them up their arses, in Mobile.

Oh, the old dun cow is dead in Mobile,
But the children must be fed,
So they milk the bull instead, in Mobile.

Oh, the eagles they fly high in Mobile,
And they shit right in your eye,
So thank God the cows can't fly, in Mobile.

Oh, the parson he has come in Mobile,
With the word of Kingdom Come,
He can stuff them up his bum, in Mobile.

Oh, I know a parson's daughter in Mobile,
Sought her, caught her, fucked her, taught'er,
Now I cannot pass my water, in Mobile.

There's no shortage of good beer in Mobile,
And they give us damn good cheer,
Oh, thank God that we are here in Mobile.

There's a lovely girl called Dinah in Mobile,
For a fuck there's no one finer,
'Cos she's got the best vagina in Mobile.

There's a lady they call Susan in Mobile,
And her cunt she's always usin'
She's got the best infusion in Mobile.

There's a man called Lanky Danny in Mobile,
And his instinct is uncanny,
When he's fingering a fanny, in Mobile.

There's a tavern in the town in Mobile,
Where for half a fucking crown,
You can get a bit of brown, in Mobile.

Oh, the girls all wear tin pants in Mobile,
But they take them off to dance,
Just to give the boys a chance, in Mobile.

There's excess of copulation in Mobile,
They relax for stimulation,
On mutual masturbation, in Mobile.

The CO is a bugger in Mobile,
And the Adj he is another,
So they bugger one another, in Mobile.

There's a shortage of good bogs in Mobile,
They wait until it clogs,
Then they saw it off in logs, in Mobile.

There's no paper in the bogs in Mobile,
So we'll wait until it clogs,
Then we'll saw it off in logs, in Mobile.

There's a bum-boy they call Hunt in Mobile,
And he thinks he's got a cunt,
'Cos his arsehole's back to front, in Mobile.

In Matruh

There's a tavern in the town in Matruh
There's a tavern in the town of Matruh
There's a tavern in the town,
Where you lay your money down
And you get a bit of brown
In Matruh.

There's a shortage of good bints in Matruh.
There's a shortage of good bints in Matruh.
There's a shortage of good bints,
So you pull it till you wince,
Then you tie it up in splints,
In Matruh, in Matruh, in Matruh.

Other verses as in 'Mobile'.

Arseholes Are Cheap Today

(Tune – La Donna E Mobile)

Arseholes [Young girls] are cheap today,
Cheaper than yesterday.
Little boys [girls] are half a crown,
Standing up or lying down.
Bigger boys [girls] are two and six,
[Larger ones are three and six,]
For they know better tricks. ['Cos they take larger dicks,]
And one at five bob [For a very large knob].

Some are wreathed in smiles,
Others are sore with piles,
The one for me,
Is the one that's free,
Tallyho! Tallyho!
What a lovely sight,
Half a mo, half a mo,
While I have a shite.

The Mole Catcher

In Manchester City by the sign of The Plough,
There lived a mole catcher, I can't tell you how.

Chorus   *With his la ti lie diddle and his la ti lie day.*
             He'd go out mole catching from evening 'til night
             And a young fellow would come for to visit his wife.

Now the mole catcher got jealous of all the same thing
And he hid under the wash house to see what did come in.

Now this young fellow comes climbing over the stile
And the mole catcher's watching, with a crafty smile.

He knocks at the door and this he does say,
"Where is your husband, good woman, I pray?"

"He's gone out mole catching, you have nothing to fear."
Little did she know the old bastard was near.

They went up the stairs and she gives him the sign,
But the filthy old fellow did creep up behind.

Now just as the young fellow reached the height of his frolics,
The mole catcher grabbed him quite fast by the bollocks.

The trap it squeezed tighter, the mole catcher did smile,
"Here's the best mole we've caught in a while."

"I'll make you pay well for ploughing me ground:
This little prank will cost you all of ten pound."

"Oh!" says the young fellow, "Christ, Gov, I don't mind,
For it only works out at tuppence a grind."

So come all you young fellows and mind what you're at,
Don't ever get caught in a mole catcher's trap.

Daniel and the King

Now it came to pass that the King came unto the prophet Daniel where he abode in the lion's den and spake unto him, saying, "How is it with thee, O Daniel?" And Daniel answered and said unto the King,

"Lo, O King, it locks."

"What locks?" asked the King, suspecting naught.

"Bollocks!" roared Daniel: and the drinks were on the King.

And on the second day, the King came again unto Daniel and spake again unto him, saying, "How is it with thee, O Daniel?"

And Daniel answered and said unto the King, "It tickles."

"What tickles?" asked the King, for he feared no ill.

"Testicles!" roared Daniel, and once again the drinks were on the King.

Now the King became exceeding vexed and betook to himself a plan whereby he might fool the prophet: and on the third day, he came again unto Daniel and spake again unto him, saying, "O Daniel, how is it with thee in yonder hole?"

But Daniel, being wiser than the King, stole the punchline the King had devised so he fell not into the trap the King had layeth by saying unto him, "What hole, O King?" Straight away he roared, "Arsehole!" and on the third day, again the drinks were on the King.

Now Daniel, being weary of these visitations, on the fourth day took unto himself a dollop of lion's dung of the bigness of a cubit and did hurl it at the King and smote him betwixt the eyes.

"SHIT!" said the King, and the whole court bent their knees and STRAINED, for that they dared do no other.

Here endeth the lesson.

How the Money Rolls In

My Father's an apple pie vendor,
My Mother makes synthetic gin,
My Sister walks out of an evening,
(My Sister sells kisses to Sailors)
And Gosh! How the money rolls in!
OR
My Father's a black market grocer,
(My Father makes book on the corner)
My Mother sells illegal gin,
My Sister sells sin on the corner,
KeeRist! How the money rolls in!

CHORUS   *Rolls in, rolls in*
                 My Gosh! How the money rolls in, rolls in,
                 Rolls in, rolls in,
                 My Gosh! How the money rolls in.

My Mother's a bawdy house keeper
Every night when the evening grows dim
She hangs out a little red lantern
My God! How the money rolls in!

My Brother's a slum Missionary,
Wot saves fallen women from sin,
He'll save you a blonde for a guinea
My God! How the money rolls in.

My Brother lies over the ocean,
My Sister lies over the sea,
My Father lies over my Mother,
And that's how they got little me.

My Sister's a barmaid in Sydney
For a shilling she'll strip to the skin
She's stripping from morning to midnight
My God! How the money rolls in!

My Cousin's a Harley Street surgeon
With instruments long, sharp and thin,
He only does one operation,
My God! How the money rolls in!

My Grandad sells cheap prophylactics
And punctures the teats with a pin
For Grandma gets rich on abortions
My God! How the money rolls in.

Uncle Joe is a registered plumber,
His business is holes and in tin,
He'll plug your hole for a tanner.
My God! How the money rolls in.

My Uncle is carving out candles
From wax that is surgically soft
He hopes it will fill up the gap
If ever his business wears off.

I'd an Uncle who was a night watchman,
Who spent all his nights in the pit,
He used to come home in the mornings,
All covered all over with shit.

One night was so dark and so stormy,
When Uncle went down to the pit,
The wind went and blew out his candle,
And Uncle fell down in the shit.

Poor Uncle he never recovered,
From the accident down in the pit.
His funeral takes place tomorrow,
He'll be buried in six feet of shit.

My Aunt keeps a girls' seminary
Teaching young girls to begin
She doesn't say where they finish
My God! How the money rolls in!

I've lost all me cash on the horses,
I'm sick from the illicit gin,
I'm falling in love with my Father,
MY GOD! What a mess I am in!

My one skin lies over my two skin,
My two skin lies over my three,
My three skin lies over my four skin,
So pull back my four skin for me.

Pull back, pull back,
Oh! Pull back my four skin for me, for me,
Pull back, pull back,
Oh! Pull back my four skin for me!

A Yorkshire Airfield

(Another to the tune of 'Clementine')

On an airfield, a Yorkshire airfield,
Close beside the railway line,
Dwelt a Squadron, a Hali Squadron,
Who were always off on time.

Now this Squadron, this Hali Squadron,
Who were always off on time,
Never fly high, never fly low,
For as civvies they do dine.

Here at Selby, at The Londeborough,
They do yearly meet and dine,
Exchange newses with each other,
Cheerio now, till next time.

The Old Monk

There was an old Monk of great renown,
There was an old Monk of great renown,
There was an old Monk of great renown,
Who chased the young girls all around the town.

CHORUS   *The old sod – the dirty old sod,*
               The bastard deserves to die,
               Fuck him. Let us pray,
               Glory, glory, Hallelujah.   *SHIT!*

He met a girl with fair blue eyes,
He met a girl with fair blue eyes,
He met a girl with fair blue eyes,
And curly hair between her thighs.

He took her to his Marble Hall,
He took her to his Marble Hall,
He took her to his Marble Hall,
And showed her pictures upon the walls.

He laid her on his lily-white bed,
He laid her on his lily-white bed,
He laid her on his lily-white bed,
And shagged her and shagged her until she was dead.

His brother monks they cried in shame,
His brother monks they cried in shame,
His brother monks they cried in shame,
So he turned her over and shagged her again.

His brother monks to stop his frolics,
His brother monks to stop his frolics,
His brother monks to stop his frolics,
They took a bloody great knife and cut off his bollocks.

And now he's lost all sexual desire,
And now he's lost all sexual desire,
And now he's lost all sexual desire,
He stays at home and pulls his wire.

The Monk of Great Renown

There was a Monk of great renown,
There was a Monk of great renown,
There was a Monk of great renown,
Who shagged an innocent maid from town.

CHORUS   The sod, the old sod,
          The bugger deserves to die.

His brother Monks they cried in shame,
So he turned her over and shagged her again.

He met another by the mill,
And shagged and shagged her up the hill.

He met another in the hay,
And put her in the family way.

He took her to the Abbot's bed,
And shagged and shagged till she was dead.

But when the Abbot cried, "Amen",
He shagged her back to life again.

His brother Monks to stop his frolics,
Put a nail through his prick and cut off his bollocks.

And now the moral I will tell,
And now the moral I will tell,
When all the world just looks like hell,
Just shag and shag till all is well.

All The Nice Girls Love A Candle

(Tune – Ship Ahoy)

All the nice girls love a candle,
All the nice girls love a wick,
For there's something about a candle,
That's just like a young man's prick.
Nice and greasy, goes in easy,
It's a lady's pride and joy.
It's been up the Queen of Spain,
And it's going up again,
Ship ahoy! It's a boy!

Monte Carlo

(Tune – The Man Who Broke the Bank at Monte Carlo)

As she walked along the Bois de Bologne
With a heart as heavy as lead,
She wished that she was dead.
She had lost her maidenhead.
Her heart in a funk and covered with spunk,
Her knickers were torn and her cunt was worn,
She's the girl who lowered the price at Monte Carlo.

As he walked along the Bois de Bologne
With his prick upon the stand,
The girls all say, "It's grand
To take it in their hand."
You give them a bob and they're on the job,
Pulling the foreskin over the knob
Of the man who broke the Bank at Monte Carlo.

She Went for a Ride in a Morgan

She went for a ride in a Morgan:
She sat with the driver in front:
He fooled with her genital organ:
The more vulgar-minded say, "Cunt."

Now she had a figure ethereal.
She auctioned it out to men's cocks
And contracted diseases venereal:
The more vilgar-minded say, "Pox."

The dazzling peak of perfection,
There wasn't a prick she would scorn.
She gave every man an erection.
The more vulgar-minded say, "Horn."

Did you ever see Anna make water?
It's a sight that you ought not to miss:
She can leak for a mile and a quarter
The more vulgar-minded say, "Piss."

If I had two balls like a bison
And a prick like a big buffalo,
I would sit on the edge of creation
And piss on the buggers below.

Old Boy

With baited breath the Dean undressed
The Vicar's wife to lie on.
He thought it crude to do it nude
So he kept his old school tie on.

She'll be Coming Round the Mountain

She'll be coming round the mountain when she comes,
She'll be coming round the mountain when she comes,
She'll be coming round the mountain,
Coming round the mountain,
Coming round the mountain when she comes.

CHORUS   *Singing Aye, Aye, Yippee, Yippee-Ay,*
          [I will if you will, so will I]
          Singing Aye, Aye, Yippee,
          Aye, Aye, Yippee,
          Aye, Aye, Yippee, Yippee-Ay.

Oh! She'll be wearing silk pyjamas [khaki issue] when she comes,
She'll be wearing silk pyjamas when she comes,
She'll be wearing silk pyjamas,
Wearing silk pyjamas,
Wearing silk pyjamas when she comes.

Oh! She'll have to sleep with Grandpa when she comes,
She'll have to sleep with Grandpa when she comes,
She'll have to sleep with Grandpa,
Oh! She'll have to sleep with Grandpa,
She'll have to sleep with Grandpa when she comes,

She'll be all wet and sticky when she comes,
She'll be all wet and sticky when she comes,
She'll be all wet and sticky,
Icky, Icky, Icky,
She'll be all wet and sticky when she comes.

Nelson and Hood

This is our [my] story, this is our [my] song,
We've [I've] been in the Air Force too blooming long,
Where are our pilots when Jerry's about?
They sit in the hangar, they sing and they shout,
And they talk about things they know fuck-all about,
And they're boozing, bloody well boozing,
So bring out the Nelson the Rodney and Hood,
For our fucking Air Force is no fucking good.

There were other verses such as:

Bring out the Nelson, Rodney and Renown,
It's no use saying the Hood 'cos the bugger's gone down.

Alouette

Alouette, Alouette, gentile Alouette,
Alouette je te plumerai,

Chanter plumerai la tete

followed by verses with:

et le bec
et la bouche
et le tits etc?
et le RUDE WORDS
et le MUCH MORE RUDERY

Alouette, je te plumerai.

This song is originally French Canadian (1879) and I remember hearing it sung brilliantly (complete with actions) at RAF Merryfield, Ilminster, by 242 Sqdn CO, Ving Commander Vischt (Swiss) early in 1946.

The 'ole in the Ark

One evening at dusk, Noah stood on his Ark,
Putting green oil int' starboard side lamp.
His wife came along and said, "Summat's wrong,
Our cabin is getting quite damp."

Said Noah, "Is that so?" Then he went down below
And he found t'were right, what she said,
For on the floor, quite a puddle he saw.
It were slopping around under t'bed.

Said he, "There's a hole int'bottom somewhere,
We must find it before we retire."
Then he thought for a bit and he said, "Ha! That's it,
A bloodhound is what we require."

So he went and fetched bloodhound from t'place where it lay,
'Tween skunk and polecat it were,
And as things down below were a trifle so so,
It were glad of a breath of fresh air.

They followed the hound as it sniffed around,
Until they located the leak.
It were a round hole in the side about two inches wide,
Where a swordfish had poked in its beak.

By Gum! How the wet squirted in through that 'ole,
While young Shem, who at sums were expert,
Worked it out on his slate, it came in at the rate
Of one gallon per second per squirt.

The bloodhound tried hard to keep t'water in check
By lapping it up wi' his tongue,
But as that were no go, he went up to t'hole
And shoved in his nose for a bung.

But that faithful poor hound, he were very near drowned
As they dragged him away none too soon.
The fountain that rose, he had worked up his nose
And blew him up like a balloon.

And then Mrs Noah shoved her elbow in t'hole
And said, "I've stopped it, I believe,"
But they found very soon, that she'd altered her tune,
'Cos the water had gone up her sleeve.

Then finding her elbow weren't doing much good,
She said, "Noah, I've got an idea,
You sit on the leak and by the end of the week,
There's no knowing, the weather may clear."

Noah didn't think much to this idea at all,
But reckoned he'd give it a try.
On the hole down he flopped and the leaking all stopped
And all except him were quite dry.

They took him his breakfast and dinner and tea,
As day after day there he sat,
'Till the storm had all passed and they landed at last
On the top of Mount Ararat.

And that's how Noah got them all safe ashore,
But ever since then, strange to tell,
Them as helped him save t'Ark, have all carried a mark,
Aye, and all their descendants as well.

That's why a dog has a cold nose and a lady cold elbows.
You'll also find if you enquire,
That's why a man takes coat tails in hand
And stands wi' his back to t'fire.

No Balls At All

Oh! Gather round lovers and listen to me:
I'll tell you a tale that will fill you with glee:
There was a young maiden – so pretty and small:
She married a man who had no balls at all.

CHORUS *Balls, balls*
No balls at all,
A very short penis
And no balls at all.

The night they were married, they crept into bed ...
Her cheeks they were rosy, her lips they were red ...
She felt for his penis – his penis was small ...
She felt for his balls – he had no balls at all!

The night of the wedding she got into bed.
She sighed with lust, her cheeks were quite red.
She felt for his tool and his tool was quite small.
She felt for his balls – he'd got no balls at all!
No balls, no balls at all,
She'd married an Airman with no balls at all!

"Oh! Mother, dear Mother, O what can I do?
I've married a man who's unable to screw,
There is not another with penis so small!
Moreover my husband has no balls at all!"

"Oh! Daughter, sweet Daughter, do not be too sad,
The very same trouble I had with your Dad.
There's many a bounder who'll answer the call
Of the wife of the man who has no balls at all."

This pretty sad Maiden took Mother's advice:
She found the procedure exceedingly nice!
A bouncing big baby was born in the Fall:
The poor little bastard had no balls at all!

No Balls At All #2

Come you old drunkards give ear to my tale,
This short little story will make you turn pale.
It's about a young lady – so pretty and small.
Who married a man who had no balls at all.

CHORUS   *Balls, balls, no balls at all,*
She married a man who had no balls at all.

How well she remembered the night they were wed.
She rolled back the sheets and crept into bed.
She felt for his prick, how strange, it was small.
She felt for his balls, he had no balls at all.

Mammy, Oh! Mammy, Oh! Pity my luck.
I've married a man who's unable to fuck.
His tool bag is empty, his screwdriver's small,
The impotent wretch has got no nuts at all.

Daughter, my daughter, now don't be a sap.
I had the same trouble with your dear old Pap.
There's many a man who'll come to the call
Of the wife of the man who has no balls at all.

The pretty young girl took her Mother's advice
And found the whole thing exceedingly nice,
An eleven pound baby was born in the Fall,
But the poor little bastard had no balls at all.

Ode to the Four Letter Word

Banish the use of the four letter word,
Whose meanings were ever obscure,
The Angles and Saxons, those bawdy old birds,
Were vulgar, obscene and impure.

When Nature is calling, plain speaking is out,
When Ladies (God Bless 'em) are milling about,
You may wee wee, make water or empty the glass,
You may powder your nose, even Johnnie may pass.

Shake the dew off the lily, see a man re a dog,
Change the Dickie birds' water, or go to the bog,
But please do remember if you would know bliss,
That only in Shakespeare do characters piss.

A woman has bosoms, a bust or a breast,
Those lily-white swellings that bulge 'neath her vest,
Twin domes of ivory, sheaves of new wheat,
In a moment of rapture, ripe peaches to eat.

You may speak of her nipples as fingers of fire,
With hardly a question of drawing her ire,
But by Rabelais beard, she will throw seven fits,
If in good honest English you refer to her tits.

It's a cavern of joy we're thinking of now,
A warm fertile plain awaiting the plough,
A quivering pigeon caressed by your hand,
Of the National Anthem (it makes all men stand).

Maybe it's a grotto, a haven of rest,
A beautiful flower, a moss-covered nest,
But friend, heed this warning, beware of affront,
By aping the Saxon, don't call it a cunt.

Although she's a lady, she'll often be kind,
If you intimate kindly just what's on your mind,
You may tell her your're hungry, your nerves highly strung,
You may ask her to see how your etchings are hung.

Stick your pin in her cushion, you might even try,
Put the lid on the saucepan, or even lay might get by,
But the moment you're forthright, get ready to duck,
For the girl isn't born who will stand for, "Let's fuck!"

So banish the words that Elizabeth used,
When she was a Queen on her throne,
The modern maid's virtue is easily bruised,
By four letter words on their own.

Though your morals are loose as an Alderman's vest,
If your language is always obscene,
Your acts matter not, your word is the test,
Of the vulgar, impure and unclean.

Ollie, Ollie, Ollie

Ollie, Ollie, Ollie,
With his balls on a trolley
And his cock tied up in string,
Sitting on the grass
With a bugle up his arse,
Trying to play, "God Save the King!"

Ode to the Four Letter Word #2

Banish the use of the four letter words
Whose meanings are never obscure.
The Angles and Saxons, those bawdy old birds,
Were vulgar, obscene and impure.
But cherish the use of the wheedling phrase
That never says quite what you mean:
Far better be known by your hypocrite ways
Than as vulgar, impure or obscene.

When nature is calling, plain speaking is out,
When ladies, God Bless 'em, are milling about.
You may "Wee-wee", "Make water", or "Empty the glass",
You can "Powder your nose", even "Widdle" may pass.
"Shake the dew off the lily", "Phone your Grandma",
"See a man about a dog" – you've not gone too far,
But please to remember, if you should know bliss,
That only in Shakespeare do characters 'piss'.

A woman has "Bosoms", a "Bust" or a "Breast",
Those "Lily white swellings" that bulge 'neath her vest,
Are "Twin towers of ivory" – "Sheaves of new wheat",
In moments of passion, "Ripe apples to eat".
You may speak of her nipples as "Fingers of fire"
With hardly a question of raising her ire,
But I'll bet you a bob she'll throw two thousand fits
If you speak of them blandly as good honest "tits".

It's a "Cavern of joy" you are thinking of now.
A "Warm tender field awaiting the plough".
It's a "Quivering pigeon" caressing your hand,
Or the "National Anthem" (it makes us all stand!)
Or perhaps it's a "Flower", a "Grotto" or "Well",
"The hope of the world" or a "Velvety Hell",
But friend, heed the warning, beware the affront,
Of aping the Saxons – don't call it a "cunt".

Though the lady repels your advances, she'll be kind
As long as you intimate what's in your mind.
You may tell her you're "Hungry", you "Need to be swung".
You may ask her to see "How your etchings are hung"
Or mention the "Ashes that need to be hauled",
"Put the lid on her saucepan", even that's not too bald,
But the moment you're forthright, get ready to duck,
For the wench isn't weaned who'll stand for "Let's fuck!"

So banish the words that Elizabeth used
When she was the Queen on the Throne.
The modern maid's virtue is easily bruised
By the four letter words all alone.
Let your morals be as loose as an Alderman's vest
If your language is always obscure:
Today not the act , but the word is the test
Of the vulgar, obscene or impure.

Pacific Lament

You can keep your scattered islands
And your skies of Asian Blue.
You can keep your aircraft carriers
And their dim commanders too.
You can keep the dusky maidens
With their skirts of waving grass.
You can keep the whole Pacific
And stuff it up your arse !

This Old Coat of Mine

This old coat of mine,
The inside is quite fine,
But the outside's seen some dirty weather.

So I'll cast this coat away
Until the blooming day
Roll on the ship that takes me home.

This old collar of mine,
The inside is quite fine,
But the outside's seen some dirty weather.

So I'll cast this collar away
Until the blooming day
Roll on the ship that takes me home.

This old tie of mine,
The inside is quite fine,
But the outside's seen some dirty weather.

So I'll cast this tie away
Until the blooming day
Roll on the ship that takes me home.

This old shirt of mine,
The inside quite fine,
But the outside's seen some dirty weather.

So I'll cast this shirt away
Until the blooming day
Roll on the ship that takes me home.

AND SO ON until the strip-tease is completed

How Much to Oldham?

In Market Street, Manchester, one Summer night,
There was only one cab on the rank.
The driver was reading the *News of the World*
And quietly enjoying a wank.

He was dreaming that Venus was kissing his penis,
The shaking was making him tired,
When a waitress called Lena, with tits like Sabrina,
Came over and gently enquired.

"How much will you charge me to Oldham?"
The cab driver nearly dropped dead.
He got such a shock, he let go of his cock
And 'Barclayed' his gear knob instead.

He said, "That's alright, I'm not busy tonight,
You're a nice sort of girl, I can tell,
So I won't charge you nothing to 'old 'em,
If you'll let me 'old yours as well!"

B Flight

"B" Flight was the bullshit Flight,
Arsed about a lot,
But when it came to the exams,
"B" Flight came out top.

***Found written on a window frame
at No 5 ITW Torquay in 1941***

Lady Astor's Speech

The following are extracts from a speech by Lady Astor in the House of Commons during a debate on Rights for Women ... Allegedly!

"We want what the men have. It may not be much but we want it. We will have it without friction, or, if we cannot have it through our organisations, we will have it through our combinations, or without them if necessary."

"Men say we cannot grasp the potentialities, many and varied are men's arguments about us. They have driven their most prominent points into us again and again."

"We refuse to be poked in the gallery and insist on being put down on the floor of the House."

"Are we going to take it lying down? No! We will take it with our backs to the wall ..."

"Some say, "Down with skirts", but we say, "Up with skirts and down with trousers", then we shall see things as they really are."

"There is little difference between men and women." (Voice in the gallery – "Three cheers for the little difference!")

"Furthermore, as long as we are split as we are, men will always want to get on top of us."

"They block us in the House, they block us everywhere."

"But we must change our position. We must get on top."

After this, a man got up and pressed his point home.

He won, hands down.

Penguin

(Tune – MacNamara's Band)

I never fly in aircraft 'cos I haven't got the guts,
I sit upon my arse all day and write out lots of bumph,
The Aircrew call me "Penguin", 'cos I haven't any wings,
I'm one of the Chairborne Airmen, shiny pants and shiny rings.

CHORUS   *If the flak went bang, my knees would clang,*
                My ring would blaze away,
                My head would whirl, my tail would curl,
                I'd run the other way,
                *For I'm absolutely useless when it comes to fighting
wars,*
                *I can only sit upon my arse and wear holes in my
drawers.*

I stand and watch the Aircrew when they take off for a flight,
And thank the Lord I'll not be there when searchlights probe the
night,
I've never had to corkscrew, I've never had to weave,
The only thing that I can do is stop the Aircrew leave.

Just now I'm a practising upon the barrack square,
To get the boys a marching like they fly up in the air,
One day there'll be a parade, a bloody big parade,
And in front of all the Aircrew goes the shiny-arsed brigade.

We work from nine till five each day, with two breaks off for tea,
I've never had an engine cut, and feathering's Greek to me,
When Aircrew come and see us, we nearly throw a fit,
The only thing that we can do is sign a clearance chit.

I'd hate to be sent out one night upon a ruddy op,
My heart would sink into my boots, I'm sure my guts would drop,
But the AOC comes up to me and takes me by the hand,
And promises me another ring, to stay upon the land.

He Tried Me on the Sofa

He tried me on the sofa,
He tried me on the chair,
He tried me on the window-sill,
But he couldn't get it there.

He tried me on the verandah,
I stood against the wall,
I even sat upon the floor,
But it would not act at all.

He worked it back and forwards,
He tried both front and rear,
But it was all too useless,
His thing was out of gear.

He tried it this and that way,
And oh, how I did laugh
To see how many ways he tried
To take my photograph ...

My Little Pink Panties

(Tune – When You Wore a Tulip)

[I wore my panties, my little pink panties,
And he wore his GI shorts]
When you wore a tulip, a bright yellow tulip
And I wore a red, red, rose.
He began to caress me,
And then he undressed me,
What a thrill we had in store.

He played with my titties,
My little pink titties
And down where the short hairs grow.
His kisses grew sweeter,
He pulled out his Peter
And whitewashed my little red rose.

Pickeldy Pickeldy Pox

(Tune – Home on the Range)

CHORUS   *Pickeldy, pickeldy pox,*
Pry the lid from the herring box.
You are never forlorn,
When you're gilding the horn
At the brothel in East Grimsby Docks.

Oh! Give me a home where the prostitutes roam
And your knackers hang down to your knees,
Where the babies are born with a fifteen inch horn
And pox is the favourite disease.

Oh! Give me a den that is mainly for men,
Where the whores dance to fiddle and fife
And they take down their drawers
For the Blacks and the Boers.
It's the damndest hothouse of your life.

The beds they all creak and the pisspots all leak
And the sheets are not always too clean,
But there's a hole in the floor
For the lame and the poor
And for women a fucking machine.

With It In

Can you walk a little way with it in,
With it in?
Can you walk a little way with it in,
With it in?

She answered, with a smile,
I can walk a fucking mile,
With it in,
With it in,
With it in.

The Pig Song

One evening last October, when I was far from sober,
And as homeward I did wend my weary way,
[To keep my feet from wandering I tried]
My feet began to stutter, so I lay down in the gutter,
[My poor legs were all a'flutter, so I lay down in the gutter]
And a pig came up and down beside me lay.
[And a pig came up and lay down by my side.]

We talked about fair weather, when good fellows get together,
[We sang, "Never mind the weather just as long as we're together"]
And a lady passing by was heard to say,
"You can tell a man who boozes, by the company he chooses."
And the God-Damned pig got up and walked away.
[And the pig got up and slowly walked away.]

Yes the pig got up and slowly walked away
Slowly walked away, slowly walked away,
Yes the pig got up and then smiled and winked at me
As he slowly walked away.

On cattle shows I've centred, in one a pig I entered
And one day I sat down with him in his sty.
Famous people came in to visit,
When a sweet voice said, "What is it?"
I looked up and Greta Garbo caught my eye.

She said, "What a lofely fella," poked the pig with her umbrella
Then she looked at me a while and whispered, "Say!
Yeah, ay tink dis iss hees brudder" – at my side I felt a shudder
And the pig got up and slowly walked away.

Yes the pig got up and slowly walked away
Slowly walked away, slowly walked away,
Yes the pig got up and then smiled and winked at me
As he slowly walked away.

The Great Plenipotentiary

(Recitation)

The Bey of Algiers when afraid for his ears,
A messenger sent to our Court, Sir:
As he knew in our State that the women have weight,
He chose one well hung for good sport, Sir.
He searched the Divan till he found out a man,
Whose bollocks were heavy and hairy,
And he lately came o'er from the Barbary Shore,
As the Great Plenipotentiary.

When to England he came with his prick all aflame,
And showed to his Hostess on landing,
Whence spread its renown to all parts of the town,
As a pintle past all understanding.
So much there was said of its snout and its head,
They called it the great Janissary,
Not a Lady could sleep till she got a sly peep
At the Great Plenipotentiary.

As he rode in his coach, how the whores did approach,
And they stared as if stretched on a tenter:
He drew every eye of the dames that passed by,
Like the wonderful sun to its centre.
As he passed through the town, not a window was down,
And the maids hurried out just to see:
And the children cried, "Look! – At the man with the cock,
That's the Great Plenipotentiary."

When he came to the Court, O what giggle and sport!
Such squinting and squeezing to view him!
What envy and spleen in the women were seen,
Of the happy and pleased that got to him.
They vowed in their hearts, if men of such parts
Were found in the Coast of Barbary,
Twas a shame not to bring a whole guard for the King,
Like the Great Plenipotentiary.

The dames of intrigue formed their cunts in a league,
To take him in turn like good folk, Sirs:
The young misses' plan was to catch as catch can,
And all were resolved on a stroke, Sirs!
The cards to invite flew by thousands each night,
With bribes to his old Secretary,
And the famous Eclipse was not let for more leaps
Than the Great Plenipotentiary.

When his name was announced, how the women all bounced,
And the blood hurried up to their faces:
He made them all itch from the nave to the breech,
And their bubbies burst out of their laces.
There was such damned work to be fucked by the Turk,
That nothing their passion could vary:
The whole Nation fell sick for the Tripoli prick
Of the Great Plenipotentiary.

The Duchess whose Duke made her ready to puke
With fumbling and frigging all night, Sir,
Being first with the prize was so pleased by its size,
That she begged to examine its plight, Sir!
"Good God!" cried Her Grace, "its head's like a mace!
'Tis as big as a Corsican Fairy!
I'll make up – please the pigs – for dry-bobs and frigs,
With the Great Plenipotentiary."

And now to be bored by this Ottoman Lord,
Came a virgin far gone in the wane, Sir:
She resolved for a try, though her cunt was so dry
That she knew it would split like a cane, Sir!
True, it was as she spoke – it gave way at each stroke,
But O what a terrible quandery,
With one mighty thrust her old piss-bladder bust
On the Great Plenipotentiary.

The next to be tried was an Alderman's bride,
With a cunt that would swallow a turtle,
Who had horned the dull brows of her Worshipful spouse,
Till they sprouted like Venus's myrtle.
Through thick and through thin, bowel deep he dashed in,
Till her quim frothed like cream in a dairy,
And expressed by loud farts, she was strained in all parts
By the Great Plenipotentiary.

The next to be kissed by Plenipo's lift
Was a delicate maiden of honour,
She screamed at the sight of his prick in a fright,
Though she had the whole place upon her:
"Cunt Jesus," she said, "what a prick for a maid,
Do pray come and look at it Mary."
Then she cried with a grunt, "O he's ruined my cunt
With his Great Plenipotentiary."

Two sisters came next – Peg and Mary by name,
Two ladies of very high breeding,
Resolved one would try while the other stood by
To assist in the bloody proceeding:
Peg swore by her God that the Musselman's knob,
Was thick as the buttocks of Mary,
"But I'll have one drive if I'm ripped up alive
By the Great Plenipotentiary."

All twats were bewitched and just longed to be stitched,
Even Fairies would languish and linger,
And the boarding school miss as she sat down to piss
Drew a Turk on the floor with her finger.
By fancy so struck they clubbed round for a fuck,
And bought a huge candle and hairy,
And the teachers from France they fuck'd the distance,
With the Great Plenipotentiary.

Each sluice-cunted bawd who was knocked all abroad,
Till her premises gaped like the grave, Sir,
Hoped her luck was on, so she'd feel the Turk's dong,
As all others were lost in her cave, Sir.
The nymphs of the stage his fine parts did engage,
Made him free of the grand feminary,
And gentle Signors opened all their back doors
To the Great Plenipotentiary.

Of love's sweet reward measured out by the yard,
The Turk was most blessed of Mankind, Sir,
For his powereful dart went home to the heart,
Whether stuck in before or behind, Sir.
But no pencil can draw this long-donged Pawshaw
That each cunt-loving contemporary,
But as pricks of the game let's drink health to the name
Of the Great Plenipotentiary!

Your Baby has Gone Dahn the Plug'ole

A woman was bathing 'er baby one night,
The youngest of seven, the poor little mite.
The Muvver was poor and the baby was fin,
'Twas only a skeleton covered wiv skin.
The Muvver turned round for the soap on the rack,
She was only a moment, but when she looked back,
'Er baby 'ad gorn. In anguish she cried,
"Oh, where is my baby?" The Angels replied,
"Your baby 'as gorn dahn the plug'ole,
"Your baby 'as gorn dahn the plug.
The poor little thing was so skinny and fin,
It should 'ave bin barfed in a jug.
Your baby is perfecly 'appy,
You don't see its face any more,
Your baby 'as gorn dahn the plug'ole,
Not lorst, jist gorn before."

Ring The Bell, Verger

(Tune – Bloody Great Wheel)

Verger in t'Belfry stood,
Grasped in 'is 'and 'is mighty pud,
From afar t'Vicar yells,
"Stop pullin' t'pud, pull t'fookin' bells."

Up in t'belfry t'Sexton stands,
Pulling t'pud wi' grimy 'ands,
Down in t'Vestry t'Vicar yells,
"Stop pullin' t'pud – pull t'fookin' bells!"

CHORUS   *Ring the bell, Verger, ring the bell, ring,*
Perhaps the congregation will condescend to sing,
Perhaps the village organist, sitting on his stool,
Will play upon the organ and not upon his tool.

Down in t'belfry t'Chauffeur lies,
Vicar's wife between his thighs.
Voice from t'pulpit from afar,
"Stop fookin t'wife, start t'fookin' car".

'Andsome Butler, pretty Cook,
Down in t'pantry 'avin' fook,
Up in t'parlour t'Mistress she squeals,
"Stop fookin' t'Cook – cook t'fookin' meals!"

Out in t'garage, t'Chauffeur lies,
Firmly clasped by t'Mistress' thighs,
Master says, "Ah, there you are,
Stop fookin' t'wife, start t'fookin' car!"

Ocean liner, six days late,
Stoker stoking stoker's mate,
Voice from t'Captain o'er the wire,
"Stop pokin' t'mate, start pokin' t'fire!"

She Was Poor But She Was Honest

(Various versions seriously merged!)

CHORUS   *It's the syme the whole world over,*
                    It's the rich wot gets the gryvy,
                    It's the poor what gets the blime.

OR   *It's the same the whole world over,*
                    It's the poor wot gets the blame,
                    It's the rich wot gets the pleasure,
                    Ain't it all a bleedin' shame.

She was poor but she was honest,
Victim of a rich man's whim,
First he fucked her, then he left her,
And she had a child by him.

She was poor but she was honest,
Victim of a Squire's whim,
First he kissed her, then he upped her,
And she had a child by him.

See him with his hounds and horses.
See him strutting at his club,
While the victim of his whoring
Drinks her gin inside a pub.

See her on the bridge at midnight,
Throwing snowballs at the moon,
She said, "George, I never 'ad it,"
But she spoke too fucking soon.

[Standin' on the bridge at midnight,
Cracking walnuts with her crutch,
She said, "Jack, I've never 'ad it,"
He said, "No? Not fucking much!"]

[See her on the bridge at midnight,
Picking blackheads from her crutch,
She said, "Jack, I never 'ad it."
He said, "No? Not fucking much!"]

Then she came to London City,
To recover her fair name,
But another bastard fucked her,
Now she's on the streets again.

[Then she came to London City,
Just to hide her bleedin' shyme,
But a Labour Leader fucked her,
Put her on the streets agine.]

[So she ran away to London
For to 'ide 'er grief and shime,
There she met another Squire
And she lost 'er nime agine.]

See 'er ridin' in 'er carriage
In the Park so bright and gay,
Where the nibs and nobby persons
Come to pass the time of diy.

See him riding in a carriage,
Past the gutter where she stands,
He has made a stylish marriage,
While she wrings her ringless hands.

In a Banker's arms she flutters
Like a bird wot's broke a wing.
First 'e loved 'er the 'e left 'er,
Still she 'asn't got a ring.

Then there came a wealthy pimp,
Marriage was the tale he told,
She had no one else to take her,
So she sold her Soul for gold.

See 'im in 'is splended mansion
Entertainin' with the best,
While the girl wot 'e 'as ruined
Entertains a payin' guest.

See 'im drivin' to the Races
To the Ascot Gold Cup 'unt,
While the girl wot 'e disgraces
Earns a livin' through 'er cunt.

See him sitting at the theatre,
In the front row with the best,
While the girl that he has ruined
Entertains a sordid guest.

See her stand in Piccadilly,
Offering her aching quim,
She is now completely ruined,
It was all because of him.

[Now she stands in Piccadilly,
Pickin' blackheads from her quim,
She is now completely ruined,
And it's all because of him.]

See 'er standin' in the gutter
Sellin' matches by the box,
Any man wot tried to up 'er
Is bound to get a dose of pox.

So she went into the country,
Where she tried to hide her shyme,
There she met an Army Captain,
And lost her nyme agyne.

See the little country cottage,
Where her simple parents live,
Though they drink the fizz she sends 'em,
On her aching quim they live. [But they never can forgive.]

She got the pox and 'orrid chankers,
From the wolves that plumbed her gut,
So she went down to the river,
For to give her whorin' up.

See her on the bridge at midnight,
Saying, "Farewell blighted love,"
Then a scream, a splash, Oh! Goodness!
What is she a'doing of?

As they dragged her from the river,
Water from her clothes they wrung,
And they thought that she had had it,
But the corpse got up and sung.

See him seated in his Bentley (Rolls Royce),
Coming homeward from the hunt,
He got riches from his marriage,
She got corns upon her cunt.

See him in the House of Commons,
Passing Laws to banish crime,
While the victim of his passion,
Walks the streets in filth and slime.

See him in the House of Commons,
Passing Laws for all mankind,
While she walks the streets of London,
Selling chunks of her behind.

In the Violet Time

Violate me in the violet time, in the vilest way you know,
Ruin me, ravage me, brutally savage me,
On me no mercy show.

Don't give me a man who is selfish and treacherous,
I want a man who is generous and lecherous,
Violate me in the violet time, in the vilest way you know.

The Airman's Prayer

The first thing we'll pray for, we'll pray for some beer,
Glorious, glorious, glorious beer!
If we only have one beer, may we also have ten,
May we have a whole brewery? Said the airmen, "Amen!"

The next thing we'll pray for, we'll pray for some girls,
Glorious, glorious, glorious girls!
If we only have one girl, may we also have ten,
May we have a whole harem? Said the airmen, "Amen!"

The next thing we'll pray for, we'll pray for the King,
Glorious, glorious, glorious King!
If he only has one son, may he also have ten,
May he have a whole Squadron? Said the airmen, "Amen!"

The next thing we'll pray for, we'll pray for the Erk,
The poor wretched blighter who does all the work,
And if he only serves one year, may he also serve ten,
May he serve for blinking ever? Said the airmen, "Amen!"

A WAAF's Lament

I wish I were a fascinating bitch,
I'd never be poor, I'd always be rich.
I'd live in a house with a little red light,
I'd sleep all day and work all night.

And every month, I'd have a week off
To make the customers wild:
I'd rather be a fascinating bitch
Than an illegitimate child.

There Was A Priest

(Tune – Yankee Doodle)

There was a priest a dirty beast,
His name was Alexander,
He had a prick ten inches thick,
And called it his commander.

One night he met a gypsy maid,
Her face was black as charcoal,
And in the dark he missed his mark,
And shoved it up her arsehole.

A babe was born one sunny morn,
Its face was black as charcoal,
It had a prick ten inches thick,
And a double-barrelled arsehole.

We're a shower of bastards

We're a shower of bastards,
Bastards are we,
We are 621, arseholes of the Universe.
We couldn't be worse,
For we're a shower of bastards,
We'd rather fuck than fight
For Victory.

Here's to the breezes

Here's to the breezes
That flits through the treezes
And lifts girls' chemezes
To the place that teezes and pleazes
And gives men dizeezes,
By Jeezes!

The Story of P/O Prune

This is the story of Prune poor chap,
And how he caught a dose of clap,
One stand-down night, no careless talk,
Found Prune and F/O Fixe in York [Betty's Bar]
Imagine then, it wasn't long,
Before some crumpet came along,
Prune with a smile persuaded her to stay,
With gin and lime, "Yes, Fixe will pay."
Prune, through his red-rimmed eyes,
Surveyed her shapely knees and thighs,
"If I can only get her rougher
I'll take her out", he thought, "and stuff her".
They went a walk around the Town,
And as they passed the Rose and Crown,
Prune was amazed to hear her holler,
"Here we are then – half a dollar.
For look my dear, imagine that,
Over there I have my flat!"
And once inside the shameless strumpet,
Exhibited a nifty crumpet.
Once, twice, he rode until
Despite the strokings of her hand,
He could not raise another stand.
In accents coarse, her voice much rougher,
She pronounced him as a feeble duffer,
Once back in camp, on duty bent,
Old Prune forgot this incident,
Until one day, indulging in a dip,
He noticed something on the tip,
And all the piss he tried to pass
Came scorching out like broken glass.
The MO said, "You little fool,
You really should respect this tool,
As it is I rather fear
A goodish dose of gonorrhoea."
Now let this be a warning talk,
To all who seek their crump in York.

They're Pulling The Old Pub Down

(Shout and Responses)

Caller	They're pulling the Old Pub down!
Response	BOO! (Prolonged)
Caller	They're building a new one down the road.
Response	HOORAY! (Prolonged)

Caller	It's only got one bar
Response	BOO!
Caller	A hundred yards long
Response	HOORAY!

Caller	They're not selling beer
Response	BOO!
Caller	They're giving it away
Response	HOORAY!

Caller	Whiskey's on ration
Response	BOO!
Caller	A gallon a day
Response	HOORAY!

Caller	Only one bar-tender
Response	BOO!
Caller	Ninety-nine barmaids
Response	HOORAY!
Caller	All topless!
Response	PROLONGUED HYSTERIA!

The Choric Song of the Masturbators

or LAST NIGHT or PULLA DA PUD (Tune – Finiculi Finicula)

Last night I pulled me pud
It did me good, I knew it would.

Sling it, fling it, throw it on the floor,
Smash it, crash it, catch it in the door.

Some people say that fuckin's mighty good,
But for personal enjoyment, I'd rather pull me pud.

Some go in for buggery; some think fucking's good,
But for for personal enjoyment I prefer to pull me pud.

Last night I lay in bed and pulla da pud,
It did me good, I knew it would.
Last night I lay in bed and pulla da pud,
It did me good, I knew it would.

You should see me on da short strokes,
I use dis hand, I use dis hand.
You should see me on da long strokes,
I use dis hand, I use dis hand,

Bite it, smite it, jam it in the door,
Tease it, squeeze it, bang it on the floor.

I know a forty-eight in Manchester*
Is certainly very good
But for personal enjoyment
I prefer to pulla da pud.

(*or nearest large city with 3 syllables)

The Duchess Of Lee

I had tea with the Duchess of Lee.
She said, "Do you fart when you pee?"
I replied with great wit
That I belch when I shit
(I replied with some pluck,
"Do you sweat when you fuck?")
I thought that was one up to me.

I dined with the Duchess of Lee.
She said, "Will you fuck once with me?"
I replied with great tact,
"As a matter of fact,
I have brought my French letter with me".

So I lay with the Duchess of Lee,
Her manner was open and free,
Her words to me were,
"Which do you prefer,
My arse or my cunt?
It doesn't matter to me."

I examined the Duchess of Lee
To see which side it would be,
I examined her front,
She'd a nice little cunt,
But I found it too narrow for me.

I turned over the Duchess of Lee,
And examined her backside with glee,
And oh my delight
When I found it just right,
So I lay with the Duchess of Lee.

I awoke with the Duchess of Lee,
And she said, "I'm sure you'll agree,
That oriface fundamental
Though less than sentimental
Is safer and better for me."

Ivan Skavinsky Skavar

(There are all sorts of versions and all sorts of spellings; just a few shown here).

Now the maidens of Egypt are fair to behold,
[The harems of Egypt are fine to behold]
The harlots the fairest of fair,
But the fairest, a Greek, was owned by a Sheik,
[But the fairest of all was owned by a Sheik]
Named Abdul the Bull Bull Emir.

Now a travelling brothel was brought to the town,
By a Russian who travelled afar,
He wagered a thousand to all who could out-fuck,
Did Ivan Skavinsky Skavar!

[Now a travelling brothel came down from the North
'Twas run privately for the Tsar,
Who wagered a hundred no one could out-shag
Ivan Skavinsky Scavar.]

Abdul rode by with his cock on the stand,
His balls hanging low with desire,
He wagered a thousand that he could out-fuck,
Ivan Skavinsky Skavar.

A Festival Great was arranged for the date,
A visit was paid by the Czar,
The streets were all lined and midst harlots inclined,
Sat Ivan Skavinsky Skavar.

[A day was arranged for the spectacle great,
A holiday proclaimed by the Tsar,
The streets were all lined with the harlots assigned
To Ivan Skavinsky Scavar.]

[Old Abdul came in with a snatch by his side,
His eyes bore a leer of desire,
And he started to brag how he would outshag
Ivan Scavinsky Scavar.]

The fannies were shorn and Frenchies were worn,
The starter's gun punctured the air,
People gasped with surprise when they noticed the size
Of Abdul the Bull Bull Emir.

[All hairs they were shorn, no Frenchies were worn,
And this suited Abdul by far,
And he quite set his mind on a fast action grind
To beat Ivan Scavinsky Scavar.]

They lay on their backs and opened their cracks,
[They worked all the night in the pale yellow light]
Abdul's bum revved like a car,
But he hadn't a hope against the long easy stroke
Of Ivan Skavinsky Skavar.

[They met at the track with cocks at the slack,
A starter's gun punctured the air,
They were both quick to rise, the crowd gaped at the size
Of Abdul Abulbul Amir.]

When the contest was won, Ivan wiped off his gun
And bent down to polish his spurs [the pair],
But he felt something hot, shoot into his bot,
It was Abdul the Bull Bull Emir.

All the women turned green, all the men shouted "Queen!"
They were ordered to part by the Czar,
But it was fucking hard luck, poor Abdul was stuck,
Up Ivan Skavinsky Skavar.

Now the cream of this joke as apart they were broke,
'Twas laughed at for years by the Czar,
For Abdul, poor fool, had left half of his tool,
Up Ivan Skavinsky Skavar.

Abdul Abulbul Emir

In the harems of Egypt, close-guarded and secret,
The women are of the fairest of hair,
But the very best jerk is owned by a Turk,
Called Abdul Abulbul Emir.

A travelling brothel once came to the town,
'Twas owned by a Shah from afar,
He issued a challenge to all who could fuck,
'Gainst Ivan Skavinsky Skivar.

Old Abdul arrived with his bride by his side,
He came in a bloody great car,
Bet a thousand gold lumps he'd shag many more rumps
Than Ivan Skavinsky Skivar.

They met on a track with their tools hanging slack,
The starter's gun punctured the air,
They were quick on the rise and folks gasped at the size
Of Abdul Abulbul Emir.

Although Abdul was quick at flicking his dick,
And the action was learned by the Czar,
He couldn't compete with the long steady beat,
Of Count Ivan Skavinsky Skavar.

When Ivan had won he was wiping his dong,
He stooped down to polish his peer,
He received a great root up his innocent shoot,
From Abdul Abulbul Emir.

Now Ivan had won and was polishing his gun,
And bent over to polish his pair,
When he felt something pass up his great hairy arse,
[When something red hot up his back passage shot]
It was Abdul A Bul-Bul Ameer.

Now the cream of the joke when apart they were broke,
Was laughed at for years by the Czar,
For Abdul the fool had busted his tool,
In the arsehole of Ivan Skivar.

The Puritan Mathyas

There was a Puritanical lad
And he was called Mathyas,
Who wished to go to Amsterdam
To speak with Ananyas.
He had not gone past half a mile,
But he met a Holy Sister.
He laid his Bible under her cunt,
And merrily he kissed her.

"Alas! What would the wicked say?"
Said she, "if they had seen it!
My buttocks need some bolstering,
So put the Gospels in it!
But Peace, sweetheart, for 'ere we part,
I speak from pure devotion,
By aye or nay I'll not away,
Until you taste my motion."

They made full stride with many a heave,
Until they both were tired,
"Alas!" said she, "You fuck with glee,
And my petticoats are all mired.
If we Professors of the Lamb,
To the English Congregation,
Either at Leyden or Amsterdam,
It would disgrace the Nation.

But since it is, that part we must,
Though I am much unwilling,
Good Brother have another thrust,
And take from me this shilling,
To pay your way for many a day
And feed your prick with filling."
Then down she laid, the Holy Maid
And drained him at a sitting.

Questions & Answers

Are you in good health?

Are you glad the war is over?

How long do you take getting to work?

Who's your best girl-friend?

Do you drink a lot of beer?

What's your favourite meat?

What's your favourite colour?

Do you wear suspenders?

What do you think of the weather?

Do you crave for it?

Do you get it often?

How long does it take?

With whom?

How many times a week?

Do you enjoy it?

What does it look like?

What colour is it?

Would you pay for it?

How do you feel after it?

The Souse Family

Glorious, Glorious,
One keg of beer among the four of us,
Glory to God there are no more of us,
'Cos one of us could drink it all alone.

Drunk last night
Drunk the night before
Going to get drunk tonight
Like I never got drunk before.
When I'm drunk I'm as happy as can be,
For I am a member of the Souse family.

The Souse family is the best family
That ever came over from old Germany,
The Potsdam Dutch and the Rotterdam Dutch,
The Amsterdam Dutch and the Goddam Dutch.

Drink, drink, drink, drink,
Beer, beer, beer, beer,
Foam, foam, foam, foam,
Home, home, home, home,
Sleep, sleep, sleep, sleep,
Snore, snore, snore, snore,
More, more, more, more BEER!!!
ZZ, zz, zz, zz, zz, zz.

We are, we are, we are, we are,
We are the Engineers.
We can, we can, we can, we can,
Demolish forty beers.

Drink rum, drink rum, drink rum, drink rum,
Drink rum and come with us,
For we don't give a damn for any
Man that don't give a damn for us.

The Ram of Derbyshire

(Tune – The Lincolnshire Poacher)

Now in the County of Derbyshire
There was a famous ram.
His fame was spread o'er the countryside
His prick was like a ham.

CHORUS   *And if you don't believe me*
          And you think I'm telling a lie,
          Just ask the Maids of Derbyshire
          Who'll tell you the same as I.

And when the ram was born, Sir,
He had two horns of brass,
One stuck out of his abdomen
The other stuck out of his arse.

And when the ram was young, Sir,
He had a curious trick
Of jumping over a five-barred gate
And landing on his prick.

And when the ram was middle-aged,
They carried him in a truck,
And all the Maids of Derbyshire
Came down to have a fuck.

And when the ram was old, Sir,
They put him aboard a lugger,
And all the boys of Derbyshire
Came up to have a bugger.

And when the ram was dead, Sir,
They buried him in St Paul's.
It took ten men and an omnibus
To carry one of his balls.

Rape

He grabbed me by my tender neck,
I could not yell nor scream,
He dragged me to a darkened room,
Where we should not be seen.

He took from me my flimsy wrap,
And gazed upon my form,
I was so cold, so damp and scared,
While he was hot and warm.

His fevered lips he pressed to mine,
I gave him every drop,
He drained me of my very self,
I could not make him stop.

He made me what I am today,
That's why you'll find me here,
An empty bottle thrown away,
That once was full of beer.

'Twas only an old beer bottle,
A'floating on the foam,
'Twas only an old beer bottle,
So many miles from home.
Within was a piece of paper,
With these words written on,
"Whoever finds this bottle
Will find all the beer all gone".

Red Riding Hood

CHORUS   *How could Red Riding Hood*
                   Have been so very good
                   And still kept the wolf from the door?

Father and Mother she had none,
So where in the world did the money come from?
She said she saw a wolf in Granny's bed,
With a big white sun-bonnet
Pulled down over it's head.
But you know, and I know,
What she saw instead!

What I have to ask is – who kept the basket?
The story books never tell.
They said she was a girl and so discreet,
She wouldn't pick up
Strange men in the street.
But you know and I know,
A girl's got to eat.

They said she was the smartest of girls,
She didn't need to have pearls.
But you know and I know,
What a girl does for pearls.

Mary Box

This is the tale of Mary Box,
Who gave a thousand men the pox,
Soldiers and sailors and men of honour
Fought like fiends to climb upon her,
And now that she's dead, she's not forgotten,
They dig her up and stuff her rotten.

O'Reilly's Daughter

As I was sitting by the fire,
Drinking O'Reilly's rum and water
(Drinking beer and passing water)
Suddenly a thought came to my mind,
"It's time I fucked O'Reilly's daughter."

Chorus   *Yippie-I-aye, Yippie-I-aye,*
     Yippie-I-aye for the one eyed Reilly,
     Shove it up, stuff it up, balls and all,
     Hey-jig-a-jig Tres Bon!
     (Play it on your old base drum.)

OR   *Arseholes, rissoles, balls and all,*
     Shove it up the nearest cunt!

Her hair was black, her eyes were blue,
The Colonel and the Major and the Captain sought her,
The Regimental goat and the drummer boy too,
But they never had a thump with O'Reilly's daughter.

Jack O'Flannagan is my name,
I'm the King of copulation,
Drinking beer my claim to fame,
Shagging women my occupation.

Walking through the town one day,
Who should I meet but O'Reilly's daughter,
Not a word to her did say,
But don't you think we really oughter?

Quickly up the stairs to bed,
Shagged and shagged until I stove her,
Having lost her maidenhead,
She laughed like hell when the fun was over.

Up the stairs and into bed,
Quickly cocking my left leg over,
Never a word that Maiden said,
But laughed like fuck when the fun was over.

I fucked her 'til her tits were flat,
Filled her up with soapy water,
She won't get away with that,
If she doesn't have twins, then she really oughter.

I fucked her sitting,
I fucked her lying,
If she'd been a bird,
I'd have fucked her flying!

I heard a footstep on the stair,
Who could it be but one eyed Reilly,
Fucking great pistols in his hands,
Looking for the bloke who'd shagged his daughter.

I hear footsteps on the stairs,
Old Man Reilly bent on slaughter,
With two pistols in his hand
Looking for the man who shagged his daughter.

I grabbed O'Reilly by the hair,
Stuffed his head in a bucket of water,
Rammed his pistols up his arse,
A fucking sight quicker than I'd shagged his daughter.

Come you virgins, maidens fair,
Answer me quick and true not slyly,
Do you want it fair and straight and square,
Or the way I gave it to the one-eyed Reilly?

Now O'Reilly's dead and gone,
He will haunt us all no longer,
But his daughter carries on,
Looking for the man who stopped her water.

[We took the lid of his coffin off
To mend a hole in the shithouse door, Sir.]

My Ring A-Rang A-Roo

(As I was walking down the street
A fair young maid I chanced to meet
She said to me, "How do you do,
Would you like to play with my Ring-a-rang-a-roo?")

A Maiden fair who had never been screwed,
She went to bed with a man half nude.
He took off her clothes and her cami-knicks too,
And played all night with her Ring a-rang a-roo.

CHORUS   *Your Ring a-rang a-roo, now what is that?*
"It's something warm like a pussy cat,
All covered with hair and split in two,
That's what I call my Ring a-rang a-roo."

(I took her to her Father's house.
We crept inside quiet as a mouse,
We went upstairs and I kissed her too,
And played all night with her Ring-a-rang-a-roo.)

Her Father came and her Father said,
"You've gone and lost your maidenhead,
So pack your grip and baggage too,
And earn your living with your Ricky Dan Do."

She went to town a rollicking whore,
She hung a sign outside her door
"Ten Dollars down, no less will do,
(From sweet sixteen to ninety-two)
To have a go at my Ring a-rang a-roo."

A policeman knocked upon her door,
"Have you a licence to be a whore?"
She said, "No Sir, but I'll tell you what I'll do,
You can come and have a go at my Ring a-rang a-roo."

One day there came a son of a bitch,
Who'd got the pox and seven year's itch,
He had the crabs and clinkers too
And he had a go at her Ring a-rang a-roo.

The boys all came, the boys all went,
The price came down to fifteen cents,
From sweet sixteen to seventy-two,
All had a go at that Ring a-rang a-roo.

Now nine days passed and they all felt sick
And spots appeared upon their pricks.
They vowed that they – oh, never more,
Would whang it up a ruddy little whore.

Then six months passed and they felt well,
All resolutions went to hell,
Met her again, what could they do
But whang it up her Ring a-rang a-roo?

Now after all, they're not to blame,
For Adam and Eve were just the same.
He chased poor Eve with his big bamboo
And whanged it up her Ring a-rang a-roo.

Love One

A WAAC song from the USA?

Darling you can't love one,
Darling you can't love one,
You can't love one and still have fun.
Darling you can't love one.

Darling ... two and still be true.

Darling ... three and still be free.

Darling ... four if you're not a whore.

Darling ... five and stay alive.

Ring-A-Dang-Do

When I was young and in my teens,
I met a girl from New Orleans.
Oh! She was young and pretty too
And she had what's known as a RING-A-DANG-DO.

CHORUS   *Oh! Ring-a-dang-do, pray what is that?*
           It's round and soft like a pussy cat.
           It's round and soft and enticing too,
           And that's what's known as a Ring-a-dang-do.

She took me down into her cellar,
She said I was a nice young feller.
She gave me wine and whiskey too
And let me play with her Ring-a-dang-do.

She took me up upon her bed,
And placed a pillow beneath my head.
She took me by my Whicky-wacky-woo
And shoved it into her Ring-a-dang-do.

Her Mother said, "You naughty girl,
You've gone and lost your maiden curl.
The only thing left for you to do
Is to make some dough with your Ring-a-dang-do."

So Mary went and became a whore,
She hung a sign outside her door:
"Come all ye old and young ones too
And take a crack at my Ring-a-dang-do."

Oh! Many came and many went,
And the price went down to fifty cents.
The last one came, I know not who,
But he sure played hell with her Ring-a-dang-do.

Old Dirty Mitch, the son of a bitch,
Whose arse was crowned with the seven year's itch,
A dose of syph and clapped up too,
He stuck it into her Ring-a-dang-do.

And after that they came no more,
For she was then a clappy old whore.
She took the sign down from her door
And that's the end of her Ring-a-dang-do.

Rip My Knickers Away

(Tune – Yip aye addy aye ay)

Be I Berkshire, be I buggery,
Oi koms up from Wareham.
Oi know a gal with calico drawers
And I knows how to tear 'em.

Chorus   *Rip my knickers away, away, rip my knickers away*
        I don't care what becomes of me,
        As long as you play with my c-u-n-t-e-e.

Rip my knickers away, away,
Rip my knickers away,
Down the front, down the back,
Round the cunt, round the crack,
Rip my knickers away.

Walkin' by the field one day,
I heard a maiden crying,
"Oh, please don't rip my knickers off, Jack,
You'll get there by and byin'."

Roedean School

We come from Roedean, nice girls are we,
Try to preserve our virginity:
We know the ropes, we've read Marie Stopes.
We come from Roedean School.

And when we hold our little school dance,
We always wear our little short pants.
We like to give the nice boys a chance,
We come from Roedean School.

And when the Vicar he comes to tea,
We put his hand where it shouldn't be,
We give him brandy, we make him randy,
We come from Roedean School.

Our old Headmistress, she's quite a sport,
She doesn't mind if we get caught.
We take precautions, we have our abortions,
We come from Roedean School.

The Gymn Mistress here is a terrible swell,
In the classroom she shows us as clear as a bell,
Her ideas of love stuff, but gives us the rough stuff.
We come from Roedean School.

We have a page boy, his name is Dick,
He really has a very small prick.
It's alright for keyholes and little girlie's weeholes,
But no good at Roedean School.

Our Head girl her name is Jane,
She only likes it now and again,
And again and again and again and again
And again and again and again.

We have a schoolgirl her name is Nell,
And when she drops 'em, oh how they smell!
She dropped one last Sunday which hung around till Monday,
Polluting our Roedean School.

We lie in our beds a'thinking each night,
How nice it would be to do the thing right.
We've tried all the wheezes with candles and tweezers.
It's no good at Roedean School.

And in conclusion what we expect,
Whether we're single or just a reject,
It's a quiet little nibble without any quibble,
We've been trained at Roedean School.

Aubade For The Shithouse

Come away my love with me
To the public lavatory.
There is an expert there who can
Encircle there the glittering pan.

He, happy youth, has no idea
What sufferers from diarrhoea
Expelling clouds of noisesome vapours
Spend annually on toilet papers.

But tranquilly pursues his art,
Or rocks the building with a fart.
O come away my love with me,
To the public lavatory.

Anthony Roley or ABC

(Tune – Anthony Roley)

A is for Arsehole, all covered in hair,
"Heigh Ho!" says Roley.

*CHORUS   Singing Roley Poley Gammon and Spinach,
                Heigh Ho!" says Anthony Roley.*

B is the Bastard who longs to get there,
C is the Cunt all slimy with piss,
D is the Drunkard who gave it a kiss,
E is for Eunuch with only one ball,
F is for Fucker with no balls at all,
G is for Gonorrhoea, goitre and gout,
H is the Harlot who fucks when she's sore [dishes them out]
I is the Injection for clap, pox and syph [they give you 'gainst itch]
J is the Jump of the bastard up bitch [Jerk of a dog on a bitch]
K is the King who shat on the floor,
L is the Leer of a Lecherous Licentious whore,
M is the Maiden all tattered and torn [Monk who died with the horn]
N is the Noble who gave her his horn,
[while N is the Nun he left tattered and torn]
O is the Orifice, tall, deep and wide [ready revealed]
P is for Penis all Peeled down one side,
[and P is the Penis all ready and peeled]
Q is the Quaker who shat in his hat,
R is the Roger who Rogered the cat,
S is the Shithouse that's filled to the brim,
T is the Turd that's floating therein,
U is the Usher at a virgin girl's school,
V is the Virgin who played with his tool [sucked on]
W is the Whore who thought fucking a farce,
And X, Y and Z you can stick up your arse.

Roll Me Over

(Tune as title)

Now this is Number 1 and the fun has just begun.
Roll me over, lay me down and do it again.

Now this is Number 2 and he's really getting through
[taking off my shoes]
Roll me over, lay me down and do it again.

Now this is Number 3 and his hand is on my knee,
Roll me over, lay me down and do it again.

CHORUS: *Roll me over, in the clover,*
Roll me over, lay me down and do it again.

Now this is Number 4 and he's got me on the floor
[and he's pulling off my drawers]
Roll me over, lay me down and do it again.

Now this is Number 5 and I'm really all alive
[And he's now unzipped his flies]
Roll me over, lay me down and do it again.

Now this is Number 6 And he's in an awful fix
[An he's sliding in his prick]
Roll me over, lay me down and do it again.

Now this is Number 7 and she says she is in Heaven.
Roll me over, lay me down and do it again.

Now this is Number 8 and her Father's [the Doctor's] at the gate,
Roll me over, lay me down and do it again.

Now this is Number 9 and he's [the baby's] doing [mighty] fine,
Roll me over, lay me down and do it again.

Now this is Number 10 and he wants to do it [start] again,
Roll me over, lay me down and do it again.
Now this is Number 11 and it's just the same as 7.
Roll me over, lay me down and do it again.

Back to Number 1 and he's feeling round my bum
Roll me over, lay me down and do it again.

This is Number 2 and I'm groping for him too
Roll me over, lay me down and do it again.

This is Number 3 and I can feel he's rousing me
Roll me over, lay me down and do it again.

This is Number 4 and I'm pleading for much more
Roll me over, lay me down and do it again.

This is Number 5 and I can feel my body writhe
Roll me over, lay me down and do it again.

This Number 6 and he's really giving me stick
Roll me over, lay me down and do it again.

This is Number 7 as he carries me to Heaven
Roll me over, lay me down and do it again.

This is Number 8 I want to stop, but it's too late
Roll me over, lay me down and do it again.

This is Number 9 and I'm four weeks over time!
Roll me over, lay me down and do it again.

This is Number 10 and the bastard's done it again!
Roll me over, lay me down and do it again.

Roll Me Over In The Clover #2

Now this is Number ONE and the fun has just begun.
Roll me over, lay me down and do it again.

CHORUS: *Roll me over, in the clover,*
Roll me over, lay me down and do it again.

Now this is Number TWO and he's got me in a stew.
Now this is Number THREE and his hand is on my knee.
Now this is Number FOUR and he's got me on the floor.
Now this is Number FIVE and his hand is on my thigh.
Now this is Number SIX and he's got me in a fix.
Now this is Number SEVEN and we're in our Seventh Heaven.
Now this is Number EIGHT and the Nurse is at the gate.
Now this is Number NINE and the twins are doing fine.
Now this is Number TEN and we're at it once again.
Oh! This is Number ELEVEN and we start again from SEVEN.
Oh! This is Number TWELVE and she said, "Nu kan jag sjalv."
Oh! This is Number TWENTY and she said that that was plenty.
Oh! This is Number THIRTY and she said that was dirty.
Oh! This is Number FORTY and she said, "Now you ARE naughty."

Lord St Clancy

When Lord St Clancy became a Nancy
It did not please the family fancy,
And so in order to protect him
They did inscribe upon his rectum,
"All commoners must now drive steerage,
This arsehole is reserved for Peerage."

Boat Ballad

This is the tale of Archie Moss,
Who always seemed a trifle cross,
When e's approached without due warning,
Upon each gloomy morning.

Now Archie holding F/Lt Rank,
Had bags of paisces in the bank,
But was he happy? No, not he,
A boat was all he wished to see.

From which you'll gather and it's true,
That he was very nearly due
For repat after having done,
Four years beneath the tropic sun.

Each day unfailing he'd enquire,
From Cypher whether they'd a wire,
Imparting all the usual griff,
For him to pack his bags forthwith.

Daily the answer that they gave,
"You've had it chum!" made Archie rave,
And shout and swear and cuss his lot,
And call the SPSO a clot.

The daily scene and constant strain,
Quite quickly turned poor Archie's brain,
The MO (formerly his friend),
Certified him as round the bend.

So Archie didn't get his schooner,
But went to the Mental Home at Poona,
The moral's clear and likewise true,
Get the boat, 'ere it gets you.

Salome

(The FIRST verse is as I remember it. HB)

Salome, Salome, you should see Salome,
Standing there with her tits all bare,
Every little wiggle makes the boys all stare,
She swings it, she flings it,
The boys all murmur, "Oh!",
Standing there with her tits all bare,
The old Sphinx sits and winks and winks,
Down where the sandbags grow.

Oh Salome, Salome, you should see Salome,
Standing there with her arsehole (cunt all) bare,
Waiting for someone to slide it there,
To slide it and glide it right up her fucking cunt, (shute,)
Two great balls and a chancre tall and a foreskin full of shit.
[Two black balls and a chankered knob and a foreskin full of shit]
She's a big fat sow, she's thrice the size of me.

Down our street we had a merry party,
Everybody there was oh so gay and hearty,
Talk about a treat, plenty to eat,
We drank all the beer in the boozer down the street.

There was old Uncle Joe, fair fucked up,
So we put him in the cellar with the old bull pup.
Little sonny Jim, trying to get it in,
With his arsehole winking at the moon.

She's a big fat cow, thrice the size of me,
Hairs on her belly like the branches on a tree,
She can, run, jump, fight, fuck,
Wheel a barrow, push a truck.
That's my girl, Salome.

On Monday night she takes it up the back,
Tuesday night she reels in all the slack,
Wednesday night she has a spell,
Thursday night she fucks like Hell!
On Friday she takes it up her nose,
In between her fingers, down between her toes,
Saturday night she dishes out wanks, (gams,)
And she goes to Church on Sundays.

Jesus wants me for a Sunbeam,
And a bloody fine Sunbeam am I.

Roll Your Leg Over

CHORUS   *Roll your leg over,*
Oh, roll your leg over,
Oh, roll your leg over,
The man in the moon.

I wish all the girls were like little red vixens,
And I were a fox, then I'd certainly fix 'em.

I wish all the girls were like cows in the pasture,
And I were a bull, I would run that much faster.

I wish all the girls were like sheep in the clover,
And I were a ram, then I'd ram them all over.

I wish all the girls were like little white kittens,
And I were a Tom cat, I wouldn't wear mittens.

I wish all the girls were really good skiers,
Instead of beer-drinkers and constant pee-ers.

Salome #2

(Fleet Air Arm version)

Down our street we had a merry party,
Everybody there was also gay and hearty,
Talk about a treat, we ate all the meat,
We drank all the beer from the boozer down the street.

There was old Uncle Joe, he was fair fucked up,
So we put him in the cellar with the old bull pup,
Little sonny Jim was trying to get it in,
With his arsehole winking at the moon.

Oh, Salome, Salome, that's my girl, Salome,
Standing there with her arse all bare,
Waiting for someone to slide in there,
Oh, slide it and glide it,
Right up her fucking shute,
Two brass balls with the shankers too,
And a foreskin full of shit.

She's a big fat cow, twice the size of me,
She's got hairs on her belly like the branches of a tree,
She can, run, jump, fight, fuck,
Wheel a barrow, push a truck.
That's my girl, Salome.

On Monday night she takes it up the back,
Tuesday night she hauls in all the slack,
Wednesday night she has a spell,
Thursday night she fucks like Hell,
On Friday she takes it up her nose,
In between her fingers, down between her toes,
Saturday night she dishes out gams,
And she goes to Church on Sundays.

I just want to be a Sunbeam,
And a fucking fine Sunbeam am I – Sunbeam am I.

Salvation Army

CHORUS   *To the Citadel – QUICK – MARCH!*
Come and join us! Come and join us!
Come and join our happy throng!

"Sister Anna – YOU'LL carry the banner!"
"But I carried it last time."
"Well, you'll carry it *this* time, and don't bloody argue!"

"Sister Cox – YOU'LL carry the box!"
"But I carried it last night."
"Well you'll carry it tonight, tomorrow night,
    and every *other* bloody night!"

"Sister Tucker – YOU'LL carry the other fucker!"
"But I'm in the family way!"
"You're in every bastard's way!"

"Sister Nellie – You've got a hole in your belly!"
"Well, so would you if you carried the banner for forty flaming years."

"I am an ex-Naval Officer. I used to stand on Street corners and associate with the wrong kind of women. But now I have seen the LIGHT. I have reformed! I feel so happy I could put my foot right through that BLOODY DRUM!"

Last Class

Last class was the best class,
This class is all my arse,
Last class gave me a gold watch,
This class gives me the fucking shits!
Class, Dismiss!

Sammy Hall

Oh, my name is Sammy Hall, Sammy Hall,
Oh, my name is Sammy Hall, Sammy Hall,
Oh, my name is Sammy Hall, and I've only got one ball,
But it's better than fuck-all.

CHORUS   *Damn your eyes, Blast your Soul,*
          Bloody Hell, SHIT!

Oh, they say I killed a man, killed a man,   *[repeat]*
For I hit him on the head with a fucking great lump of lead,
And now the bastard's dead.

And they say I'm to be hung, to be hung,   *[repeat]*
And they say I'm to be hung for a crime I've never done,
And they can stick it up their bum.

So the Sheriff he will come, he will come,   *[repeat]*
So the Sheriff he will come, with his finger up his bum,
'Cos he cannot get his thumb.

And the Jury they'll come too, they'll come too,   *[repeat]*
And the Jury they'll come too, in their nice new suits of blue,
'Cos they've got fuck-all else to do.

Then the Parson he will come, he will come,   *[repeat]*
Then the Parson he will come, though he looks so fucking glum,
With his tales of Kingdom Come.

And now they're hanging me, hanging me,   *[repeat]*
And now they're hanging me, Oh! Someone set me free!
This suspense is killing me.

And now I am in Hell, am in Hell,   *[repeat]*
And now I am in Hell, but it's all a'fucking well,
'Cos the Parson's here as well,

Damn his eyes, Blast his Soul, Bloody Hell, SHIT!

• •

Last Saturday Night

(Tune as title)

When I came home last Saturday night as drunk as I could be,
I saw a hat upon the peg where my hat ought to be.
I said to my wife, my darling wife, "I hope you are true to me,
Whose hat is that upon the peg where my hat ought to be?"

She said, "You're drunk you cunt, you silly old cunt,
You're as drunk as a cunt can be,
For that's a pudding basin your Mother gave to me."
Now all the world I've travelled, ten thousand miles or more,
But a basin [chamber pot] with a hat-band, I've never seen before.

When I came home last Saturday night as drunk as I could be,
I saw a coat upon the bed where my coat ought to be.
I said to my wife, my darling wife, "I hope you are true to me,
Whose coat is that upon the bed where my coat ought to be?"

She said, "You're drunk you cunt, you silly old cunt,
You're as drunk as a cunt can be,
For that's a blanket your Mother gave to me."
Now all the world I've travelled, ten thousand miles or more,
But a blanket with brass buttons on I've never seen before.

When I came home last Saturday night as drunk as I could be,
I saw a head beside the head where my head ought to be.
I said to my wife, my darling wife, "I hope you are true to me,
Whose head is that upon the bed where my head ought to be?"

She said, "You're drunk you cunt, you silly old cunt,
You're as drunk as a cunt can be,
For that's a turnip your Mother gave to me."
Now all the world I've travelled, ten thousand miles or more,
But a turnip with a moustache on, I've never seen before.

Bawdy Ballads

When I came home last Saturday night as drunk as I could be
I saw a thing beside the thing where my thing ought to be.
I said to my wife, my darling wife, "I hope you are true to me,
Whose thing is that upon the bed where my thing ought to be?"

She said, "You're drunk you cunt, you silly old cunt,
You're as drunk as a cunt can be,
For that's a rolling pin your Mother gave to me."
Now all the world I've travelled, ten thousand miles or more,
But a rolling pin with bollocks on I've never seen before.

[I saw a mess upon her nightdress where my old mess should be
That's not a mess upon my dress, but clotted cream you see]

Sunday, Monday Or Always

Won't you tell me true,
Can I fly with you
Sunday, Monday or always?

Won't you tell me when,
We shall fly again,
Sunday, Monday or always?

No need to tell me that the bloody thing won't go:
No need to tell me that she's flying left or right wing low.

So, if you're satisfied
I will take a ride,
Sunday, Monday or always!

I Took My Wife For A Scramble

I took my wife for a ramble,
A ramble along a shady lane,
She caught her foot in a bramble,
A bramble, and arse over bollocks she came.

CHORUS   *Singing,*
          Ay jig a jig, Ay jig a jig, follow the band,
          Follow the band all the way, singing,
          Ay jig a jig, Ay jig a jig, follow the band,
          Fall in and follow the band.

OR   *Hey jig a jig, fuck a little pig, follow the band etc.*

I asked her if she was offended, offended,
I asked her if she was in pain,
Before she could answer, could answer,
She was arse over bollock again.

She'd only one arm in her shimmy, her shimmy,
She'd only one leg in her drawers,
She'd only one hair on her titty, her titty,
Her old man had only one ball.

Don't Say No

Oh my darling, don't say no,
Onto the sofa you must go.
Up with your petticoat,
Down with your drawers,
You tickle mine
And I'll tickle yours.

Three Harlots of Baghdad

(*Tune: Robbers' Song from* Chu Chin Chow*)*

We are three harlots of Baghdad [of the Strand].
We fuck and we fornicate like mad.
[We own the biggest brothel in the land.]
We don't give a rap
For a dose of the clap,
Our object is to spread disease.
Syphilee, gonorhee.
Our object is to spread disease.

You can have it standing up or lying down,
You can have it either way for half-a-crown,
Up the back, up the front,
Up the navel, up the cunt.
We highly recommend a bit of brown.
Syphilee, gonorhee,
Our object is to spread disease.

Not 'quite' how I remember the ending:

For we don't give a rap
For syph or clap
Our object is to spread disease,
D-i-s-e-a-s-e, d-i-s-e-a-s-e,
Our object is to spread disease.

Me No Likee Blitish Sairor

(Tune – What a friend we have in Jesus)

Me no likee Blitish sairor,
Yankee sairor come ashore.
Me no likee Blitish sairor,
Yankee sairor pay one dollar more.

Yankee sairor call me "Honey Darling",
Blitish sairor call me "Fucking Whore",
Me no likee Blitish sairor,
Yankee sairor won't you come ashore?

Yankee sairor always wear Flench retter,
Blitish sairor never wear fuck-ore.
Me no likee Blitish sairor,
Yankee sairor won't you come ashore?

Yankee sairor have one fuck and finish,
Blitish sairor fuck for evermore.
Me no likee Blitish sairor,
Yankee sairor won't you come ashore?

Kiss Me Goodnight Sergeant Major

Kiss me goodnight Sergeant Major,
Tuck me in my little wooden bed.
We all love you, Sergeant Major,
When we hear you bawling, "Show a leg!"

Don't forget to wake me in the morning,
Bring me up a nice hot cup of tea.
Kiss me goodnight Sergeant Major,
Sergeant Major be a Mother to me!

Sweet Violets

(Tune – My Bonnie Lies Over the Ocean)

Phyllis Quat she died in the Springtime,
She expired in a terrible fit,
We fulfilled her last dying wish, Sir,
She was buried in six feet of ...

Chorus   *Sweet Violets, sweeter than all the roses,*
            Covered all over from head to toe,
            Covered all over with –SHIT

Phyllis Quat kept a sack in the garden.
I was curious I must admit,
One day I stuck in my finger
And pulled it out covered in...

Phyllis Quat took a bag to her boy friend's
But the bag was old and it split
Now the boy friend and Phyllis have parted
For the bag was packed quite full of...

I sat on a gold lavatory
In the home of the Baron of Split,
The seat was encrusted with rubies
But as usual the bowl contained...

There was a professional farter
Who could flatulate ballads and airs,
He could poop out the Moonlight Sonata
And accompany musical chairs, singing...

One day he attempted an opera,
It was hard but the fool wouldn't quit,
With his head held aloft he suddenly coughed
And collapsed in a big heap of SHIT.

Well, now my song it is ended
And I have finished my bit
And if any of you feel offended,
Stick your head in a bucket of SHIT!

Please Don't Burn Our Shithouse Down

Please don't burn our shithouse down,
Mother has promised to pay,
Father's away on the ocean blue,
And Flo's in the family way.

Brother dear has gonorrhoea,
Times are fucking hard,
So please don't burn our shithouse down,
Or we'll all have to shit in the yard.

In her eyes there was passion,
As she stood there so bare,
On her body was nothing,
But a small bunch of hair.

As he took down his trousers,
She said, "You've got your share,"
When she finally went,
She went home with the rent.

And a few bob to spare.

So, PLEASE don't burn ...   (as above.)

Bengal Blues

Back home they say we're doing OK.
Back home they say we're doing fine.
Back home they say we're doing OK.
Life's full of women and wine.

They've never heard of prickly heat,
Jungle sores or Bengal feet,
Oh me, oh my, when I get home
I'm certainly going to put them wise.

I've Got Sixpence

I've got sixpence, jolly, jolly, sixpence,
I've got sixpence to last me all my life,
I've got tuppence to spend
And tuppence to lend
And tuppence to send home to my wife.

Chorus   *No cares have I to grie-eve me,*
                    No pretty little girl to decei-ive me,
                    I'm as happy as a King belie-eve me,
                    As I go ro-o-olling home!
                    Blind Drunk! [Shouted]

I've got fourpence, jolly, jolly, fourpence,
I've got fourpence to last me all my life,
I've got tuppence to spend
And tuppence to lend
And fuck-all to send home to my wife.

I've got tuppence, jolly, jolly, tuppence,
I've got tuppence to last me all my life,
I've got tuppence to spend
And fuck-all to lend
And fuck-all to send home to my wife.

I've got fuck-all jolly, jolly, fuck-all,
I've got fuck-all to last me all my life,
I've got fuck-all to spend
And fuck-all to lend
And fuck-all to send home to my wife.

Good Old Beer

Here's to good old beer, drink her down, drink her down,
Here's to good old beer, that makes you feel so queer,
                      [that fills you full of cheer]
Here's to good old beer drink her down, drink her down.

Here's to good old wine, drink her down, drink her down.
Here's to good old wine, that makes you feel so fine,
Here's to good old wine, drink her down, drink her down.

Here's to good old whiskey, drink her down, drink her down,
Here's to good old whiskey, that makes you feel so frisky,
Here's to good old whiskey, drink her down, drink her down.

The Sparrer

There was a bleedin' sparrer lived up a bleedin' spart,
The comes a bleedin' rainstorm wot washed the bleeder art,
That bleedin' little sparrer went and sat upon the grass
And told that bleedin' rainstorm to kiss 'is bleedin' arse.
And when that storm was over and likewise too the rain,
That bleedin' little sparrer flies up that spart again.
'E builds 'isself a bleedin' nest and lays a bleedin' egg.
The bleeder bursts inside 'is guts and trickles dahn 'is leg,
Then there comes a bleedin' sparrer 'awk wot spied 'im in 'is snuggery,
'E sharpens up 'is bleedin' claws and chews 'im up to buggery.
Then there comes a bleedin' sportin' cove wot 'as a bleedin' gun:
'E shot that bleedin' sparrer'awk and spoilt 'is bleedin' fun.
Now the moral of this story is plain enough to all:

It's:–   THEM WOT'S UP THE BLEEDIN' SPART
           DON'T GET NO FUN AT ALL!

Bawdy Ballads

Once There Was a Servant Girl

Once there was a servant girl whose name was Mary Jane,
Her mistress she was good to her, her master was the same.
They knew she was a country girl just lately from the farm,
And so they did their bloody best to keep the girl from harm.

Singing bell-bottom trousers, coats of Navy Blue,
Let them climb the rigging as his Daddy used to do.

The Forty-Second Army Corps came in to paint the town,
A band of bawdy bastards and rapists of renown.
They busted every maidenhead and staggered out again,
But they never made the servant girl who lived in Drury Lane.

Next there came the Fusiliers and a band of Welsh Hussars.
They piled into the brothels, they packed into the bars.
The maidens and the matrons were seduced with might and main,
But they never made the servant girl whose name was Mary Jane.

My Old Flo

My old Flo has a fancy for buggery,
Up her arse she can take a pretty load,
Now she's opened an academy for sodomy
Down at the bottom of The Old Kings Road.

First lady forward, second lady back,
Third lady's finger up the fourth lady's crack,
Don't get them mixed up, the short with the tall,
Lady with the bad breath, face to the wall.

Sonia Snell

(Recitation)

This is the tale of Sonia Snell
To whom an accident befell,
An accident, as will be seen,
Embarrassing in the extreme.

It happened as it does to many,
That Sonia went to spend a penny,
And entered with a modest grace,
The properly appointed place.

There behind the railway station,
She sat in silent meditation,
But sad to say she did not know,
(Unfortunately unacquainted)
The seat had been varnished an hour ago.
(The seat had recently been painted.)

Poor Sonia soon came to realise
Her inability to rise,
Although she struggled, pulled and yelled,
She found that she was firmly held.

She raised her voice in mournful shout,
"Please, someone, come and get me out!"
Her cries for help very quickly brought,
A crowd of every kind and sort.

The crowd stood round and feebly sniggered,
A signalman said, "I'll be jiggered,"
"Gor blimey," said an ancient porter,
"We ough'er soak er orf wiv wa'er."

The station-master and his staff
Were most polite and did not laugh.
They tugged at Sonia's hands and feet,
But could not shift her off the seat.

A carpenter arrived at last,
And finding Sonia still stuck fast,
Remarked, "I know what I can do!"
And neatly sawed the seat in two.

Sonia arose, only to find,
She'd a wooden halo on behind,
But an ambulance drove down the street,
And bore her off complete with seat.

They took the wooden-bustled gal,
Off quickly to the hospital,
And seizing her by hands and head,
Laid her face down upon a bed.

The doctors came and cast their eyes
Upon the seat with some surprise.
A surgeon said, "Upon my word,
Could anything be more absurd?

Have any of you, I implore,
Seen anything like this before?"
"Yes," cried a student, unashamed,
"Frequently, but never framed!"

Winter Nights

Winter nights, that's the time for bombing.
Winter nights, that's the time for bombing.
Let her roar. You're over there once more: and fighting.
Winter nights, that's the time for bombing dear old Mannheim:
Let 'em drop, you can't do better.
Hear the Huns say, "Donnerwetter",
Downstairs the bombs are falling fast and Huns are running:
Upstairs, you both say, "Damn and blast", with the engines roaring:
And if she ends before you're over Bens, say fellers,
If you understand 'em – you can land 'em,
On those Winter nights.

Passengers will please refrain #1

Passengers will please refrain,
From flushing toilets while the train
Is standing in the station.
I love you.
We encourage constipation
While the train is in the station.
Moonlight always makes me
Think of you.
If you really must make water,
Kindly call the Pullman porter,
He will place the vessel
In the aisle.
If you give a brand-new quarter
To the kindly Pullman porter,
He will stand and hold your hand.
A while.

Passengers will please refrain #2

(Tune – Humoresque)

Passengers will please refrain
From passing water whilst the train
Is standing at the station or nearby:
Hoboes riding underneath,
Will get it in their hair and teeth,
And they won't like it.
Nor would I.

Whilst the train is in the station,
We encourage constipation.
A little self-control is what we need:
If you really must pass water,
Please inform the station porter,
Who will place a vessel in the vestibule:
Whilst the train is in the station,
We encourage constipation,
That is why we have to make this rule.

Gentlemen Should Please Refrain

Gentlemen should please refrain
From flushing toilets while the train
Is standing at the platform for a while.
We encourage contemplation,
While the train is in the station,
Cross your legs, grit your teeth and smile.

If you wish to pass some water,
You should sing out for a porter,
Who will place a basin in the bog.
Tramps and hoboes underneath
Get it in the eye and teeth,
But that's what comes from being underdog.

Drinking while the train is moving
Is another way of proving,
That control of eye and hand is sure.
We like our clients to be neat,
So please don't wet upon the seat
Or, even worse, don't splash upon the floor.

If the Ladies' Room be taken,
Do not feel the least forsaken,
Never show the sign of sad defeat.
Try the Gents across the hall
And if some man has felt the call,
He'll courteously relinquish you his seat.

If these efforts are in vain,
Then simply break the window pane:
This novel method's used by very few.
We go strolling through the park
A'goosing statues in the dark.
If Peter Pan can take it, why not you?

Though your clothing starts to smell,
Hear the plaintive pleading,
You must not think about relief.
Although your piles be bleeding,
Passengers will please refrain
From using toilets while the train
Is standing at the station for a while.

The Rajah-Sahib of Astrakhan

(Tune – When Johnny Comes Marching Home)

The Rajah-Sahib of Astrakhan, Yo-ho, Yo-ho,
A most licentious cunt of a man, Yo-ho, Yo-ho,
Had wives a hundred and forty-nine,
And many a favourite concubine.

CHORUS   *Yo-ho, ye buggers, Yo-ho, ye buggers,*
                Yo-ho, Yo-ho, Yo-ho.

One night he woke with the hell of a stand, Yo-ho, Yo-ho,
He called for a warrior, one of his band, Yo-ho, Yo-ho,
You bugger, you cunt, you bastard, you swine,
Go bring me my favourite concubine.
[Go down to my harem you lazy swine,
And fetch my favourite concubine.]

The warrior brought his concubine, Yo-ho, Yo-ho,
A face like Venus, a form divine, Yo-ho, Yo-ho,
[A figure like Venus, a face divine, Yo-ho, Yo-ho,]
The Rajah gave a hell of a grunt
[The Rajah gave a significant grunt]
And shoved his penis up her cunt.
[And parked his penis inside her cunt.]

The Rajah's stroke was long and slick, Yo-ho, Yo-ho,
And soon the maiden was breathing quick, Yo-ho, Yo-ho,
But just as the fuck came to a head,
The silly bugger fell through the bed.

[The Rajah's strokes were loud and long,
The maiden answered sure and strong,
But just when the ride had come to a head,
They both fell through the fucking bed.]

They hit the floor with the hell of a dunt,
Which completely buggered the poor girl's cunt,
And as for the Rajah's magnificent cock
It never recovered from the shock.

There's a moral to this tale, Yo-ho, Yo-ho,
There's a moral to this tale, Yo-ho, Yo-ho,
There's a moral to it all,
Always fuck 'em against a wall.
[If you would fuck a girl at all
Stick her right up against the wall.]

The moral to my story is, Yo-ho, Yo-ho,
As moral to every good tale there is, Yo-ho, Yo-ho,
When lying in bed and fucking a whore,
Don't fuck too hard or you'll land on the floor!
Yo-ho Ho Ho Ho Ho, Yo-ho you buggers, Yo-ho!

A Young Man of Zerubbubell

There was a young man of Zerubbubell
Who had one real and one Indiarubber ball,
Said his Uncle, "It's fate, it's a family trait,
Your Aunt had one real and one Indiarubber bub as well".

Long Strong Black Pudding

A is for A,
A?
L is for Long.
Long? A long.
S is for Strong.
Strong? A Long strong.
B is for Black.
Black? Strong black. Long strong black. A long strong black.
P is for Pudding.
Pudding? Black pudding. Strong black pudding. Long strong black pudding. A long strong black pudding.

***And so on, on the same lines,
with each initial of a fresh word, to the final***

S is for Sideways.
Sideways? Nightly sideways. Twice nightly sideways. Arsehole twice nightly sideways. Cat's arsehole twice nightly sideways. Sister's cat's arsehole twice nightly sideways. My sister's cat's arsehole twice nightly sideways. Up my sister's cat's arsehole twice nightly sideways. Pudding up my sister's cat's arsehole twice nightly sideways. Black pudding up my sister's cat's arsehole twice nightly sideways. Strong black pudding up my sister's cat's arsehole twice nightly sideways. Long strong black pudding up my sister's cat's arsehole twice nightly sideways. Long strong black pudding up my sister's cat's arsehole twice nightly sideways...

A long strong black pudding up my sister's cat's arsehole twice nightly (three times on Saturdays) sideways.

Behind Those Swinging Doors

It was Saturday night in an old mining town,
Jake's bar-room was merry and gay,
While far from the laughter a mother did wait,
For Pop to come home with his pay.

"What's keeping dear Father, why doesn't he come?"
The daughter exclaimed with a tear.
Her Mother replied, "I'm sadly afraid
Your Father has gone for some beer."

"The doors swing in, the doors swing out,
Where some pass in and others pass out,
Your Father, I fear, has his nose in the beer,
Behind those swinging doors; behind those swinging doors."

"Oh, I shall go and fetch him," the daughter declared,
"He shan't bring disgrace to our name,"
Then straight away she ran to the corner saloon
To save her dear Father from shame.

"Dear Father, dear Father, come home with me now,
The clock on the mantel strikes one,
Dear Mother is waiting, the rent must be paid,
Don't wait 'til your money's all gone"

Each Saturday night at the corner saloon,
The miners come in with their gold,
And Father blows all his wages for gin,
And Nellie blows home in the cold.

"Dear Mother," she wailed, "My mission I've failed,
My Father will ne'er mend his ways,"
The Mother exclaimed, "We'll suffer the shame,
It's always the woman who pays."

The doors swing in, the doors swing out,
Where some pass in and others pass out,
The story is told of a fool and his gold,
Behind those swinging doors; behind those swinging doors.

John Thomas

John Thomas was a butler tall,
He was the pride of the servants' hall,
He was the pride of the servants' hall,
'Cos he wore red plush breeches.
(Of all the types in the Servants' Hall
John Thomas was the pride of one and all,
Although he only had one ball
Inside his red plush breeches.)

CHORUS   *He wore red plush breeches   (repeat 3 times)*
          To keep John Thomas warm.
or   *[Inside those red plush breeches   (repeat 3 times)*
          That kept John Thomas warm.]

Now of all the girls in the servant host,
He loved Mary Jane the most,
She'd keep her hands as warm as toast
[She kept John Thomas warm as toast]
Inside his red plush breeches.

They went for a walk one moonlit night,
They went for a walk one starlit night,
And old John Thomas grew so tight
Inside those red plush breeches.

They found a stile to sit upon,
They found a bank to lie upon,
Next day she sewed some buttons on
To those red plush breeches.

Mary had an illegit,
Fanny green and face like shit
And every time she looked at it,
She cursed those red plush breeches.

Now Mary laid poor John a trap
And he fell for it like a sap
And now he's got a dose of clap
Inside those red plush breeches.

Street of a Thousand Arseholes

In the street of a Thousand Arseholes by the sign of the Swinging Tit,
Stood a slant-eyed Chinese Maiden whose name was Who Flung Shit.

Sweet as the scented lotus with eyes like pools of piss,
She stands there candle-wanking and a smile of Celestial Bliss.

She dreams of a lover at Hampstead and longs for one at Bow,
She thinks of the score that she's had on the floor,
When along comes Oo Flung Po.

"Come fly with me my bag of shit," he hollered, tool in hand,
"My love for you will last for ever, like snow on desert sand."

And then his anger mastered him, he poised himself with rage,
He even shit and stamped on it and his colour turned to beige.

Clutching his tool in his claw-like hand, he bashed it against the walls,
He took his hat and fucked at that, then bounced upon his balls.

Shoving his knob right up her twat, he dragged her around the streets,
Till bruised and sore and foreskin raw, he fell and gnawed her feet.

Then the emotion proved too much, he collapsed just like a sack,
With gaping quim she stood o'er him and pissed right down his back.

To the street of a thousand bastards, to the sign of the basted prat,
They bore him off in honour, the man who fucked his hat.

The slant-eyed maiden stands no more, she's gone with a rug to shit,
In the street of the Million Arseholes by the sign of the Swinging Tit.

Street of a Thousand Arseholes #2

another version

In the street of A Thousand Arseholes by the sign of the Swinging Tit,
There stands a Chinese maiden by the name of Hu Flung Shit.
Sweet as the scented lotus, with eyes like pools of piss,
She lies there in the gutter, wanking with celestial bliss.

As she dreams of her love – the bastard,
As she longs for his throbbing rod,
As she marks her score along the floor,
Up walks Scro Tum Sod.

"Come fly with me my purse of spunk,"
He hollered, prick in hand,
"My stand for you will last weeks through,
Like snow on the Gobi sand."

She lifted up her starboard tit,
And wisely scratched her snatch,
Then looked at him with a split-arsed grin,
And said, "Go fuck a Mandarin."

He clutched his prick with cow-like mitt,
And smashed it 'gainst the walls,
Took off his hat and fucked at that,
Then danced upon his balls.

At last his anger mastered him,
He pissed himself with rage,
He went and shit and stamped in it,
And his foreskin went quite beige.

Emotion quite o'ercame him,
He fell – just like a sack,
And she stood on him with a serene grin,
And pissed on the fucker's back.

The Chinese maiden wanks no more,
She arose and took on shit,
In the street of A Thousand Arseholes,
'Neath the sign of the Swinging Tit.

Three Old Ladies

CHORUS   *Oh dear, what can the matter be?*
Three old ladies locked in a lavatory
They were there from Monday 'til Saturday
And nobody knew they were there.

They said they were going to have tea with the Vicar,
They went in together because it was quicker,
The lavatory door was a bit of a sticker,
Nobody knew they were there.

The first lady's name was Elizabeth Porter,
She was the Bishop of Chichester's daughter,
She only went there to get rid of some water,
And nobody knew she was there.

The next was the Bishop of Chichester's daughter,
Who went in to pass some superfluous water,
She pulled on the chain and the rising tide caught her,
And nobody knew she was there.

The second lady's name was Amelia Spender
She stooped to do up a broken suspender
Which caught in the hair of her feminine gender
A really most painful affair.

The third lady's name was Emily Humphrey,
She stayed there because it was so comfy,
(Who settled inside to make herself comfy,)
She tried to get up but couldn't get her bum free,
And nobody knew she was there.

The fourth one's name was Celia Caution,
She went in to have an abortion,
It came away in a fucking great portion,
Nobody knew she was there.

The fifth one's name was Ermintrude Buntin,
She sat there a'fartin' and gruntin',
The attendant came and kicked her old cunt in,
Nobody knew she was there.

The sixth lady's name was Felicity Petter,
Who went in there to try out a French letter,
When she got there she found Rendell's were better,
Nobody knew she was there.

A seventh old lady was Katherine Foyle,
Who didn't live according to Hoyle,
She went to the doctors' but 'twas only a boil
And nobody knew SHE was there.

The next was the wife of a Deacon in Dover,
And though she was known as a bit of a rover,
She liked it so much she thought she'd stay over
And nobody knew she was there.

The ninth old lady was old Mrs Bickle,
She found herself in a desperate pickle,
Shut in the pay booth, she hadn't a nickel
And nobody knew she was there.

But another old lady was Mrs McBligh,
Went in with a bottle to booze on the sly,
She jumped on the seat and fell in with a cry,
And nobody knew she was there.

The last was a lady named Jennifer Trim,
She only sat down on a personal whim,
But somehow got pinched 'twixt the cup and the brim
And nobody knew SHE was there!

Did You Ever See?

Oh! I've got an Auntie Kitty
And she's only one titty,
But it's very long and pointed
And the nipple's double jointed.

Chorus　　　*Did you ever see,*
　　　　　　Did you ever see,
　　　　　　Did you ever see
　　　　　　Such a funny thing before?

I've got a Cousin Daniel
And he's got a cocker spaniel.
If you tickled 'im in the middle,
He would lift his leg and piddle.

Oh! I've got a Cousin Rupert.
He plays outside half for Newport.
They think so much about him,
They always play without him.

Oh! I've got a Cousin Anna
And she's got a grand piana
And she goes ram aram arama,
Till the neighbours say, "God Damn Her!"

The Bricklayers' Union

When the bricklayers' union struck,
Dear Old Bill was having a fuck.
Now by union rules he had to down tools.
That's what I call bad luck.

Queen of all the Fairies

(Tune – Blaze Away)

Oh! She was a cripple with only one nipple
To feed the baby on.
Poor little fucker he'd only one sucker
To start his life upon.

Chorus   *Twenty-one, never been done,*
                   Queen of all the Fairies.

Ain't it a pity she'd only one titty
To feed the baby on?
Poor little bugger, he'll never play Rugger,
Nor grow up big and strong.

And as he got older and bolder and bolder
And took himself in hand
And flipped and flipped and flipped and flipped
To the tune of an Air Force Band.

They tried him in the Infantry,
They tried him on the land and sea.
The poor little bugger had no success,
He left everything in a terrible mess,
We see no hope for him unless,
He joins the WAAF.

The Tree of Life

Come, prick up your ears and attend, Sirs, awhile:
I'll sing ye a song that will cause ye to smile:
'Tis a faithful description of the tree of life,
So pleasing for ev'ry maid, widow and wife.

This tree is a succulent plant I declare,
Consisting of only one straight stem, I swear,
Its top sometimes looks like a cherry in May,
At other times more like a filbert they say.

This tree universal all countries produce,
But till eighteen years growth 'tis not fit for use:
Then nine or ten inches – it seldom grows higher,
And that's sure as much as the heart can desire.

Its juice taken inward's a cure for the spleen,
And removes in an instant the sickness called 'Green',
Tho' sometimes it causes large tumours below:
They disperse of themselves in nine months or so.

It cures all dissentions 'twixt husband and wife,
And makes her look pleasant through each stage of life,
By right application it never can fail,
But then it is always put in through the tail.

Ye Ladies that long for the sight of this tree,
Take this invitation – come hither to me.
I have it just now at the height of perfection,
Adjusted for handling and fit for injection!

True Love

(Tune – There is a Tavern in the Town)

A Maiden young and fair was she,
Brought up in High Society,
An Airman young and bold was he,
Who brought this Maiden to despair.

Now when her apron strings hung low,
Far from her side he would not go,
But when those strings just would not meet,
He'd pass her by upon the street.

Her Father coming home one night,
He found the house without a light,
And on his way upstairs to bed,
A sudden thought came to his head.

He went into his Daughter's room
And found her hanging from a beam.
He took a knife and cut her down
And on her breast this note he found.

"I wish my baby had been born,
Then all my troubles would be gone,
So dig my grave and dig it deep
And place white lilies at my feet."

They dug her grave and dug it deep
And lay white lilies at her feet
And on her breast they put a turtle dove
To show that she had died for love.

Now listen all you Airmen bold,
A true maid's love is hard to find,
So when you find one good and true,
Don't change the old one for the new.

[Now all you maidens bear in mind
An Airman's love is hard to find,
And if you find one good and true,
Don't change the old love for the new.]

Bawdy Ballads

Gungda Din

(See MAD CAREW)

There's a dirty, stinking, piss-house to the North of Waterloo.
There's another one for ladies further down,
That is kept by Sally Tucker, for a shilling you can fuck her,
You can sleep with her for only half-a-crown.

Though she's known as Sally Tucker by those who used to fuck her,
Her real name is Talullah Johnstone Black.
She has handled many a tool from the days she first left school
And has earned a damned fine living on her back.

She's the dirtiest of bitches, by the colour of her britches
You would think that dame had never had a wash,
Yet the smell from her vagina is infinitely finer
Than any whisky, gin or rum and lemon squash.

One night she had a rattle with a sailor from Seattle
And she wondered why he hugged her so very, very close.
When he finished with his screwing she knew what he'd been doing
He'd gone and left her with a proper dose.

She gave it to her Father, who gave it to her Mother,
Who gave it to the Reverend Percy Brown,
Who gave it to his Cousin, who gave it to a dozen
And now it's halfway round the bloody town.

At last it came to pass, it reached the sailor's arse:
It travelled half way up his bloody back:
It rotted and it festered, his very life it pestered,
'Twas the vengeance of Talullah Johnstone Black.

There's a dirty, stinking sailor to the North of Waterloo
With a dose of syph that's slowly turning green.
Though he'll hack it and scratch it,
If he can e'er detatch it, he's a better man than I am GUNGA DIN!

Venal Vera

My name is Venal Vera.
I'm a lovely from Gezira
And the Fuhrer pays me well for what I do
And the news of next week's battle
I obtained from last night's rattle
On the golf course with a Brigadier from Kew.

I often have to tarry in the back seat of a gharry
It's part of my profession as a spy.
Whilst his mind's on fornication,
I'm extracting information
From the senior PSO or DSI.

I yield to the caress of the DPWS,
I get from him the low-down of the works
And when sleeping in the raw
With a Major from D4,
I learn of Britain's bargain with the Turks

On the point of his emission,
In the twenty-sixth position,
While he quivers in exotic ecstasy,
I hear of the location
Of a very secret station
From an over-sexed SC from O2E.

So the Brigadiers and the Majors
And the whiskey-soaked old stagers
Enjoy themselves away from Britain's shore,
Why should they bring victory nearer,
When then the ladies from Gezira
Provide them with a lovely fucking war?

The Good Ship Venus

[Tune: Yankee Doodle]

CHORUS　　*Frigging in the rigging'*
　　　　　Frigging in the rigging'
　　　　　Frigging in the rigging'
　　　　　There's fuck-all else to do!

OR　　　　*Frigging in the rigging,*
　　　　　Wanking on the planking,
　　　　　Masturbating on the grating,
　　　　　There was fuck-all else to do.

'Twas on the good ship Venus,
My God! You should have seen us,
The figurehead was a whore [nude] in bed
And the mast a rampant penis. [Sucking a red-hot penis.]

The Captain's name was Slugger,
He was a dirty bugger,
He wasn't fit to shovel shit
From one hold [ship] to another. [On any bugger's lugger.]

[The Skipper of this lugger,
His name was Mike McGrugger,
He wasn't fit to shovel shit,
The fornicating bugger.]

The Skipper's sister Charlotte,
A dirty little harlot,
First thing at night her twat was white,
In the morning it was scarlet.

The Captain was elated,
The crew investigated.
They found some sand in his prostate gland
And he had to be castrated.

The Captain's wife was Mabel,
And whenever she was able,
She gave the crew their daily screw
Upon the Messroom [Chartroom] [Galley] table.

[The Captain's daughter Mabel,
Though young was fresh and able
To suck and shake and fornicate
Upon the chart-room table.]

The Captain's randy [virgin] daughter,
Was swimming in the water,
Delighted squeals came as the eels
[Ecstatic squeals proclaimed that eels]
Entered her sexual quarter.

[His other little daughter,
Got shoved into the water,
Her plaintive squeals revealed that eels
Had found her sexual quarter.]

The Engineer McSandy,
By gum that man was randy,
He rubbed his prick against a brick
And shot a pint of brandy.

The Engineer McTavish,
Young girls he liked to ravish,
His missing tool's at Istanbul,
He was a trifle lavish.

The Second Engineer McCullock,
Who only had one bollock,
While trying to float a motor-boat,
He caught it in a rowlock.

The Third Engineer was Morgan,
By God! He was a Gorgon,
He'd entertain the lower deck
With tunes upon his organ.
[A dozen crows in rows
Could pose upon his sexual organ].

The Third Mate's name was Morgan,
He was a grisly Gorgon,
Three times a day he strummed away
Upon his sexual organ.

The First Mate's name was Morgan,
A veritable Gorgon,
By devious ways, through Mabel's stays,
He thrust his throbbing organ.]

The First Mate's name was Paul,
He only had one ball,
But with that cracker he rolled terbaccer
Around the cabin wall.

The Second Mate's name was Andy,
His balls were long and bandy,
They filled his cock with molten brass
For pissing in the brandy.

The Bosun's name was Andy,
By God! That man was randy,
We filled his bum with boiling rum,
For pissing in the brandy.

The Boatswain's name was Andy,
A Portsmouth man and randy,
His whopping cock broke chunks of rock,
To cool the Skipper's brandy.

The Greaser's name was Waring,
Renowned for deeds of daring,
His golden rule to insert the tool
Inside the big-end bearing.

The Stoker's name was Zember,
He had a mighty member,
He tried to shag some red-hot slag
And burned it to an ember.

A Cook whose name was Freeman,
He was a dirty demon,
He fed the crew on menstrual stew
And hymens fried in semen.

Another Cook O'Malley,
He didn't dilly-dally, [shilly shally],
He shot his bolt with such a jolt,
He whitewashed half the galley. [He wrecked the bloody galley].

● ●

'Twas in the Adriatic,
Where the water's almost static,
The rise and fall of cock and ball
Was almost automatic.

The Bosun's name was Lester,
He was the hymen tester,
Through hymens thick he shoved his prick,
And left it there to fester.

The DOCTOR'S name was Lester,
He was a virgin tester,
Through membranes thick he thrust his prick,
'Till it began to fester.

The First Mate's name was Wiggun,
By God he had a big'un,
We bashed his cock with a lump of rock
For friggin' in the riggin'.

The Bosun's name was Cropper,
Oh, Christ! He had a whopper,
Twice round the deck, once round his neck
And up his bum for a stopper.

The Mate his name was Slaughter,
He fell into the water,
He hit his cock upon a rock
And now it's two feet shorter.

The Second Mate was Carter,
My God! He was a farter,
He played anything from God Save the King,
To Beethoven's Appassionata. [Moonlight Sonata].

A homo was the Purser,
He couldn't have been worser,
With all the crew he had a screw
Until they yelled, "Oh no Sir!"

We had an Evil Surgeon,
Who didn't need no urgin',
His penis rose and wiped his nose,
Whenever he saw a virgin.

The Deckhand's name was Blighted,
He always got excited,
He filled his bunk with shit and spunk,
Whenever land was sighted.

The Lookout Mephistophorus,
He dipped his knob in phosphorus,
And stood all night to shine a light,
To guide us through the Bosphorus.

The Cabin Boy was Kipper,
A dirty little nipper,
They stuffed his arse with broken glass
And circumcised the skipper.

[The Cabin Boy, a nipper,
Was a regular Jack the Ripper,
He stuffed ...]

The ladies of the Nation
Arose in indignation
And stuffed his bum with chewing gum
- A smart retaliation!

The stewardess was Dinah,
She sprung a leak off China.
We had to pump poor Dinah's rump
To empty her vagina.

The ship's dog's name was Rover,
The whole crew did him over,
They ground and ground that faithful hound
From Singapore [Tenerife] [Calais Roads] to Dover.

We sailed to the Canaries,
The Crew thought they were Fairies,
They caught the syph at Tenerife,
And clap at Buenos Aires.

On the trip to Buenos Aires,
We Rogered all the Fairies.
We got the syph at Tenerife
And clap in the Canaries.

The Mates in the Bahamas,
Wore striped silk pyjamas,
The girls thought pricks were wooden sticks,
Not bloody great bananas.

'Twas on the China Station,
For lack of concentration,
We sank a junk with loads of spunk,
By mutual masturbation.

And so to end this serial,
For want of more material,
We'll leave this crew in Timbuctoo,
In a hospital venereal.
[I wish you luck and freedom from
Disease venereal.]

Arsehole, Charcoal

(Tune – The Vicar of Bray)

Ten tom-cats by the fireside sat,
All round a bucket of charcoal:
Said the tenth tom-cat to the ninth tom-cat:
"Let's blacken each other's arsehole."

CHORUS   *Arsehole, charcoal, charcoal, arsehole,*
          All around a bucket of charcoal,
          So one took a piece and the other took a piece
          And they blackened each other's arsehole.

Nine tom-cats by the fireside sat ... (and so on).

The Whiffenpoof Song

(Tune as title. The Air Gunners' Anthem)

To the tables down at Morney's
To the place where Louis dwells,
To the dear old Temple Bar,
I love so well.
See the Whiffenpoofs assembled,
With their glasses raised on high,
And the magic of their singing
Casts a spell.

Yes, the magic of this singing
Of the songs we love so well,
I'll be waiting and Govorniy and the rest.
We will serenade our Louis,
While life and voices last,
Then we pass and be forgotten like the rest.

We are poor little lambs who have gone astray,
Baa, Baa, Baa!
We are poor little black sheep
Who have lost our way,
Baa, Baa, Baa!

Gentlemen songsters out on a spree,
Doomed from here to Eternity,
Lord have Mercy on such as we,
Baa, Baa, Baa.

Gentlemen songsters out on a spree,
Doomed from here to Eternity,
Lord have Mercy on such as we,
Baa, Baa, Baa.

The Alderman's Daughters

An Alderman, a wealthy cit,
One morning met a man of wit:
"Dear Dick," said he, "I like your way
You're always cheerful every day.
Come dine with me, I know what's what
And have three daughters, mum of that."

"And Dick," he said, "To tell the truth,
Thou art a most bewitching youth,
Whate'er you do with ease is done,
I wish I had you for a son:
I wish, Dear Richard you'd agree
To take a wife out of my three."

Dick at this strange discourse amazed
Upon the blushing sisters gazed.
The smiling maidens owned for truth:
They had no quarrel with the youth.
"Dear Sir," said Dick, "I cannot tell
I love them all so very well,

But if their wit you'll let me try
I'll soon find out the mystery.
Just let each maid keep up her mask
Till I one single question ask.
Whether the mouth that's on your face
Or that in a more hidden place
The older is? Who answers best
Shall triumph in my happy breast."

The first-born daughter said, "In truth
I think the elder is my mouth,
Since in there are teeth of bone,
In that below, I'm sure are none."

The second said, "The seat of love
Is elder, for the mouth above,
Upon its lips no hair can show,
But I have got a beard below."

The youngest sister, smiling, said,
"I am a young and silly maid,
But yet I think the mouth above
Is older than the seat of love:
And what I say I thus evince
My upper mouth was weaned long since
And flesh and fish and bone can eat,
But my mouth below longs for the treat."

Richard on this embraced the fair
And for the youngest did declare.
He married her with great content
And never did his choice repent.

That Lovely Weekend

Thank you so much for that lovely weekend,
Those two nights in bed dear, you helped me to spend.
The smile on your face as you tickled my fan,
The thrill that you gave me as only you can.

I lay on my face dear, you played with my breast,
My two lovely bosoms with lovely brown tips,
My two slender legs squeezing right round your hips.
The time was so short dear and you had to go,
You didn't have much time to stay.
Your two balls were drumming, I thought you were coming,
Sorry I cried, but I just felt that way.

And when it was over you dropped off to sleep,
I lifted your shirt dear, to take just a peep,
And there was poor Jimmy as small as a shrimp,
Between your legs hanging so wet and so limp.
To mark the occasion we put down the date,
We should have used Rendells but now it's too late,
So please get a licence and marry me soon,
Our child will be born on the 18th of June.

The Cowboy's Whore

(Tune – Billikins and His Dinah)

Way down in Alberta where the bullshit grows thick,
Where folks chew tobacco and the cowboys come quick,
There lives young Charlotte, the girl I adore,
The Pride of the Prairie, the cowpuncher's whore.

One day on the prairie, while whittlin' a stick,
I was ridin' along with a throb in my prick,
When who should I meet but the girl I adore,
Charlotte, the harlot, the cowpuncher's whore.

She's dirty, she's vulgar, she shits in the street,
Whenever you meet her, she's always in heat.
She'll fuck for a dollar, take less or take more,
Will Charlotte the harlot, the cowpuncher's whore.

One day in a canyon, she opened her quim.
A rattlesnake saw her and flung himself in.
Now Charlotte gives the cowpunchers a fright,
The only cunt in Alberta that rattles and bites.

A lusty cowpuncher from down Texas way,
Took out his six-shooter and started to play.
He tickled her cunt with a forty-five shell
And the rattlesnake died, saying, "What fucking Hell!"

Do Your Balls Hang Low?

Do your balls hang low,
Do they dangle to and fro,
Can you tie them in a knot,
Can you tie them in a bow,
Can you sling 'em o'er your shoulder
Like a regimental soldier,
Do your balls hang low?

Seven Whores Of Pompey

(Tune – Come Comrades, Fill the Flowing Bowl)

There were seven whores of Pompey a sipping of their wine,
And the subject for discussion was "Is your thing bigger than mine?"
Now up spoke Bloody Mary, her cunt was big as Hell,
And in it was a lighthouse and a battleship as well.

The next one was a sailor's wife and she was dressed in blue,
And in one corner of her funny little thing she stowed a seaboat's crew.
She stowed a seaboat's crew my boys, the rowlocks and the oars,
And in the other corner the Marines were forming fours.

The next one was a fisherman's wife and she was dressed in green
And in one corner of her funny little thing she stowed a soup tureen.
She stowed a soup tureen my boys, the ladles and the soup
And in the other corner Naval Airmen looped the loop.

The next one was a brewer's wife and she was dressed in grey
And in one corner of her funny little thing she stowed a brewers' dray.
She stowed a brewers' dray my boys the barrels and the beer
And in the other corner she had Syph and Gonorrhoea.

The next one was a pongo's wife and she was dressed in red,
And in one corner of her funny little thing she stowed a horse's head.
She stowed a horse's head my boys, the bridle and the bit,
And in the other corner Naval Airmen shovelling shit.

The next one was a CPO's wife and she was dressed in puce,
And in one corner of her funny little thing she practised self-abuse.
She practised self-abuse my boys in forty different ways
And in the other corner was Willmott buggering Hayes.

The next one was a cricketer's wife and she was dressed in vermilion
And in one corner of her funny little thing she stowed the Lord's
pavilion.
She stowed the Lord's pavilion boys, the batsman and his duck
And in the other corner the remains of last night's fuck.

The next one was the Captain's wife and she was dressed in gold
And in one corner of her funny little thing she had the "Leopold".
She had the "Leopold" my boys, the diesels and the oil,
And in the other corner she'd a fucking 'normous boil.

* *

Then up there spake the Airman's wife and she was dressed in beige
And in one corner of her funny little thing she had a Handley Page.
She had a Handley Page my boys with joystick and its knob
And in the other corner were two Naval Airmen on the job.

Then up there spake the actor's wife who was also dressed in beige
And in one corner of her funny little thing she had the Windmill stage.
She had the Windmill stage my boys, the gallery and the stalls,
And in the other corner she had C B Cochrane's balls.

Then up there spake the observer's wife and she was dressed in chrome
And in one corner of her funny little thing she had the aerodrome.
She had the aerodrome my boys, the bombers and the troops
And in the other corner there were Wimpeys [Barras] looping loops.

And then there was the ops room girl – she was a little WAAF
And in one corner of her funny little thing she had the ops room staff.
She had the ops room staff my boys, all fucking there like Hell,
And in the other corner she had signals staff as well.

And then up spake the telephone girl and she was dressed very strange
And in one corner of her funny little thing she had the camp exchange.
She had the camp exchange my boys, the wire and all the switches
And in the other corner Little F had left his breeches.

And last there was a Lieutenant's wife, and she was dressed so poor
And in her palmy days my boys, she'd been a Pompey whore.
She'd been a Pompey whore my boys and her price was half a crown,
But now that she's got married, her price is coming down.

And these from the Army, no doubt....

Next there came the Colonel's wife and she was dressed in red,
And in her quite enormous quim she had a feather bed.
Next there came the Sergeant's wife and she was dressed in black,
And in her quite enormous quim she had a chimney stack.
Next there came a Corporal's wife and she was dressed in brown,
And in her quite enormous quim was all of Tidworth town.

Will You Marry Me?

If I give you half-a-crown,
Can I take your knickers down,
Will you marry, marry marry marry,
Will you marry me?

If you give me half-a-crown,
You can't take my knickers down,
You can't marry, marry marry marry,
You can't marry me.

If I give you fish and chips,
Will you let me squeeze your tits,
Will you marry, marry marry marry,
Will you marry me?

If you give me fish and chips,
I won't let you squeeze my tits,
You can't marry, marry marry marry,
You can't marry me.

If I give you my big chest
And all the money I possess,
Will you marry, marry marry marry,
Will you marry me?

If you give me your big chest
And all the money you possess,
I will marry, marry marry marry,
I will marry you.

Get out of the door you lousy whore,
My money was all you were looking for
And I'll not marry, marry marry, marry,
I'll not marry you.

When She Was Only Seventeen

When she was only seventeen,
She found she had a quim.
She'd sit before the looking-glass
And ease one finger in.

But now that she is forty-four,
And largely lost her charm,
She can get five fingers in
And half her fucking arm.

Three Old Whores from Winnipeg

(Tune – My Love Lies Dying)

Three old whores from Winnipeg
Were drinking sherry wine.
One said to the other,
"Your hole's no bigger'n mine."

"You're a liar!" said the other one,
"For mine's as big as the sea,
The ships sail in and the ships sail out,
And never bother me."

"You're a liar!" said the other one,
"For mine's as big as the air,
The ships sail in and the ships sail out,
And never tickle a hair."

"You're a liar!" said the other one,
"For mine's as big as the moon,
The ships sail in on the First o' the Year,
And don't come out till June."

"You're all three liars!" said the very first one,
"For mine's the biggest of all,
The ships sail in and the Fleets sail in
And never come out at all!"

They Called the Bastard Stephen

A Maiden sat in a mountain glen,
Seducing herself with a fountain pen.
The capsule broke and the ink went wild,
And she gave birth to a blue-black child.

Chorus   *And they called the bastard Stephen,*
And they called the bastard Stephen,
And they called the bastard Stephen,
'Cos that was the name of the ink.
(Quink, Quink.)

No matter how, nor where, nor when,
Use Stephen's ink in your fountain pen!

Stephen was a bonny child,
Pride and joy of his Mother mild,
And all that worried her was this;
His steady stream of blue-black piss.

Now MARY of New Brighton pier
Seduced herslef with a bottle of beer.
The top came off and the froth ran wild
And she gave birth to a nut-brown child.

Chorus   *They called the bastard Threlfalls,*
They called the bastard Threlfalls,
They called the bastard Threlfalls,
For that was the name of the beer.
(Queer, Queer.)

The Portions of a Woman

(Tune – Tangle o' The Isles)

The portions of a woman that appeal to man's depravity
Are fashioned with considerable care,
And what at first appears to be a simple little cavity,
Is really an elaborate affair.

Now surgeons who have studied these feminine phenomena,
By numerous experiments on Dames,
Have taken all the items of the gentle sex's abdomena,
And given them delightful Latin names.

There's the "Vulva" and "Vagina" and the good old "Perinaeum",
And the Hymen, which is sometimes found in brides,
There's lots of little things – you'd love 'em could you see 'em,
The Clitoris and God knows what besides.

What a pity it is then, when we common people chatter
Of those mysteries to which I've referred,
We use for such a delicate and complicated matter,
Such a very short and unattractive little word.

The erudite authorities who study the geography
Of that obscure but entertaining land,
Are able to indulge a taste for intricate topography,
And view the tasty details close at hand.

But ordinary people, though aware of their existence,
And complexities beneath the public 'know',
Are normally contented to view them at a distance,
And treat them roughly speaking as a show.

And therefore when we laymen probe the secrets of virginity,
We exercise a simple sense of touch,
We don't cloud the issue with meticulous Latinity,
But call the whole concern a simple CUNT.

For men have made this useful and intelligent commodity
The topic of innumerable jibes,
And though the name they call it by is something of an oddity,
It seems to fit the subject they describe.

Bawdy Ballads

The Woodpecker Song

(Tune – Dixie)

I stuck my finger up a Woodpecker's hole,
And the Woodpecker said, "God Bless my Soul,
Take it out, take it out, take it out. Remove it."

I removed my finger from the Woodpecker's hole,
And the Woodpecker said, "God Bless my Soul,
Put it back, put it back, put it back. Replace it."

I replaced my finger in the Woodpecker's hole,
And the Woodpecker said, "God Bless my Soul,
Turn it round, turn it round, turn it round. Revolve it."

I revolved my finger in the Woodpecker's hole,
And the Woodpecker said, "God Bless my Soul,
T'other way, t'other way, t'other way. Reverse it."

I reversed my finger in the Woodpecker's hole
And the Woodpecker said, "God Bless my Soul,
Slow it down, slow it down, slow it down. Retard it."

I retarded my finger in the Woodpecker's hole
And the Woodpecker said, "God Bless my Soul,
Speed it up, speed it up, speed it up. Increase it."

I speeded my finger in the Woodpecker's hole
And the Woodpecker said, "God Bless my Soul,
In and out with it, in and out with it. Reciprocate it."

I reciprocated my finger in the Woodpecker's hole
And the Woodpecker said, "God Bless my Soul,
That's enough, that's enough, that's enough. It's finished."

There is another ending to this one!

I retracted my finger from the Woodpecker's hole
And the Woodpecker said, "God Bless my Soul,
Take a whiff, Take a whiff, Take a whiff,
Revolting!"

West Virginian Hills

In the hills of West Virginy lived a girl called Nancy Brown,
For beauty and for virtue she was of great renown.
There came the village Deacon to Nancy one fine day,
Took Nancy to the mountains, but Nancy wouldn't play.
She came rollin' down the mountain, rollin' down the mountain,
She came rollin' down the mountain mighty wise,
For she didn't give the Deacon that there thing that he was seekin'.
She remained as pure as the West Virginy skies.

There came a rovin' cowboy with laughter and with song,
Took Nancy to the mountain, but she still knew right from wrong.
She came rollin' down the mountain, rollin' down the mountain,
She came rollin' down the mountain mighty wise,
'Cos despite the cowboy's urgin' she remained the village virgin.
She remained as pure as the West Virginy skies.

Then came Henderson, the trapper, with his phrases sweet and low,
Took Nancy to the mountain, but she still knew "Yes" from "No",
She came rollin' down the mountain, rollin' down the mountain,
She came rollin' down the mountain mighty wise,
She remained, as I have stated, quite uncontaminated,
She remained as pure as the West Virginy skies.

Then came a City Slicker with his hundred dollar bills,
Put Nancy in his Packard, and drove her to the hills,
And she stayed up in the mountain, stayed up in the mountain,
Yes, she stayed up in the mountain, all night long.
She returned next morning early, more a woman than a girlie,
And her Mother kicked the hussy out of town.

Now she's living in the city, she's living in the city,
And by all accounts she's living mighty swell,
'Cos she's wining and she's dining
And she's on her back reclining
And the West Virginy skies can go to hell.

Then came ole man Depression, kicked the slicker in the pants,
He had to sell his Packard and he had to give up Nance,
So she's gone back to the mountain, gone back to the mountain,
Yes, she's gone back to the mountain as of yore.
Now the cowboys and the Deacon,
They both get what they were seekin',
For she's just another West Virginy whore.

The Babe That I Carry

(Tune – The Girl That I Marry)

The babe that I carry will have to be
Left on the steps of a nunnery.
The boy I called my own,
Puts on roll-ons and stockings and smells of Cologne.

His toe-nails are polished, he dyes his hair,
He's known on Piccadilly as Zena Dare,
'Stead of flittin', he sits knittin'
For a policeman he met in Thames Ditton.
I must wed another, 'cos he loves my brother.
Not me!

The Fucking Thing Was Ours!

(Recitation)

The night was dark and stormy,
The wind was very strong,
As we all sat in our hutment,
While a gunner sang a song.
We were in the open country,
With some ack-ack guns as hosts,
When we heard an order shouted
And straight away took posts.
We heard a plane approaching
And thought about our town
And how the folks would treat us
If we should bring it down.
The lights from nearby sprang up
And felt around the sky,
Like the feelers of an octopus
And we all wondered why.
With all of them above us,
(They seemed to fill the air)
They never seemed to show them
To the officers standing there.
Then we had the order
And the guns all opened fire.
The noise was so terrific
As the plane went soaring higher.
We blazed away for minutes
And it seemed to stick it all,
When with a cheer we saw it
Lurch sideways, then fall.
It came crashing down towards us,
We saw it was afire,
And as it crashed behind us,
The flames went roaring higher.
We ran towards it, stood stock still,
After firing there for hours,
We saw the marks upon its side,
The fucking thing was ours!